GLENCOE
MATHEMATICS

Algebra 1

Chapter 4
Resource Masters

Glencoe
McGraw-Hill

New York, New York
Columbus, Ohio
Chicago, Illinois
Peoria, Illinois
Woodland Hills, California

Consumable Workbooks

Many of the worksheets contained in the Chapter Resource Masters booklets are available as consumable workbooks in both English and Spanish.

Study Guide and Intervention Workbook	0-07-827753-1
Study Guide and Intervention Workbook (Spanish)	0-07-827754-X
Skills Practice Workbook	0-07-827747-7
Skills Practice Workbook (Spanish)	0-07-827749-3
Practice Workbook	0-07-827748-5
Practice Workbook (Spanish)	0-07-827750-7

ANSWERS FOR WORKBOOKS The answers for Chapter 4 of these workbooks can be found in the back of this Chapter Resource Masters booklet.

Glencoe/McGraw-Hill

A Division of The McGraw-Hill Companies

ISBN: 0-07-827728-0

Algebra 1
Chapter 4 Resource Masters

2 3 4 5 6 7 8 9 10   024   11 10 09 08 07 06 05 04 03

Contents

Teacher's Guide to Using the Chapter 4 Resource Masters

The *Fast File* Chapter Resource system allows you to conveniently file the resources you use most often. The *Chapter 4 Resource Masters* includes the core materials needed for Chapter 4. These materials include worksheets, extensions, and assessment options. The answers for these pages appear at the back of this booklet.

All of the materials found in this booklet are included for viewing and printing in the *Algebra 1 TeacherWorks* CD-ROM.

Vocabulary Builder
Pages vii–viii include a student study tool that presents up to twenty of the key vocabulary terms from the chapter. Students are to record definitions and/or examples for each term. You may suggest that students highlight or star the terms with which they are not familiar.

WHEN TO USE Give these pages to students before beginning Lesson 4-1. Encourage them to add these pages to their Algebra Study Notebook. Remind them to add definitions and examples as they complete each lesson.

Study Guide and Intervention
Each lesson in *Algebra 1* addresses two objectives. There is one Study Guide and Intervention master for each objective.

WHEN TO USE Use these masters as reteaching activities for students who need additional reinforcement. These pages can also be used in conjunction with the Student Edition as an instructional tool for students who have been absent.

Skills Practice
There is one master for each lesson. These provide computational practice at a basic level.

WHEN TO USE These masters can be used with students who have weaker mathematics backgrounds or need additional reinforcement.

Practice
There is one master for each lesson. These problems more closely follow the structure of the Practice and Apply section of the Student Edition exercises. These exercises are of average difficulty.

WHEN TO USE These provide additional practice options or may be used as homework for second day teaching of the lesson.

Reading to Learn Mathematics
One master is included for each lesson. The first section of each master asks questions about the opening paragraph of the lesson in the Student Edition. Additional questions ask students to interpret the context of and relationships among terms in the lesson. Finally, students are asked to summarize what they have learned using various representation techniques.

WHEN TO USE This master can be used as a study tool when presenting the lesson or as an informal reading assessment after presenting the lesson. It is also a helpful tool for ELL (English Language Learner) students.

Enrichment
There is one extension master for each lesson. These activities may extend the concepts in the lesson, offer an historical or multicultural look at the concepts, or widen students' perspectives on the mathematics they are learning. These are not written exclusively for honors students, but are accessible for use with all levels of students.

WHEN TO USE These may be used as extra credit, short-term projects, or as activities for days when class periods are shortened.

Assessment Options

The assessment masters in the *Chapter 4 Resources Masters* offer a wide range of assessment tools for intermediate and final assessment. The following lists describe each assessment master and its intended use.

Chapter Assessment

CHAPTER TESTS

- *Form 1* contains multiple-choice questions and is intended for use with basic level students.

- *Forms 2A and 2B* contain multiple-choice questions aimed at the average level student. These tests are similar in format to offer comparable testing situations.

- *Forms 2C and 2D* are composed of free-response questions aimed at the average level student. These tests are similar in format to offer comparable testing situations. Grids with axes are provided for questions assessing graphing skills.

- *Form 3* is an advanced level test with free-response questions. Grids without axes are provided for questions assessing graphing skills.

  All of the above tests include a free-response Bonus question.

- The **Open-Ended Assessment** includes performance assessment tasks that are suitable for all students. A scoring rubric is included for evaluation guidelines. Sample answers are provided for assessment.

- A **Vocabulary Test**, suitable for all students, includes a list of the vocabulary words in the chapter and ten questions assessing students' knowledge of those terms. This can also be used in conjunction with one of the chapter tests or as a review worksheet.

Intermediate Assessment

- Four free-response **quizzes** are included to offer assessment at appropriate intervals in the chapter.

- A **Mid-Chapter Test** provides an option to assess the first half of the chapter. It is composed of both multiple-choice and free-response questions.

Continuing Assessment

- The **Cumulative Review** provides students an opportunity to reinforce and retain skills as they proceed through their study of Algebra 1. It can also be used as a test. This master includes free-response questions.

- The **Standardized Test Practice** offers continuing review of algebra concepts in various formats, which may appear on the standardized tests that they may encounter. This practice includes multiple-choice, grid-in, and quantitative-comparison questions. Bubble-in and grid-in answer sections are provided on the master.

Answers

- Page A1 is an answer sheet for the Standardized Test Practice questions that appear in the Student Edition on pages 252–253. This improves students' familiarity with the answer formats they may encounter in test taking.

- The answers for the lesson-by-lesson masters are provided as reduced pages with answers appearing in red.

- Full-size answer keys are provided for the assessment masters in this booklet.

4 Reading to Learn Mathematics

Vocabulary Builder

This is an alphabetical list of the key vocabulary terms you will learn in Chapter 4. As you study the chapter, complete each term's definition or description. Remember to add the page number where you found the term. Add these pages to your Algebra Study Notebook to review vocabulary at the end of the chapter.

Vocabulary Term	Found on Page	Definition/Description/Example
arithmetic sequence		
axes		
common difference		
coordinate plane koh·AWRD·nuht		
dilation dy·LA·shuhn		
function		
image		
inductive reasoning ihn·DUHK·tihv		
inverse		
linear equation		
mapping		

(continued on the next page)

4 **Reading to Learn Mathematics**

Vocabulary Builder *(continued)*

Vocabulary Term	Found on Page	Definition/Description/Example
origin		
quadrant KWAH·druhnt		
reflection		
rotation		
sequence		
standard form		
terms		
transformation		
translation		
vertical line test		

4-1 Study Guide and Intervention

The Coordinate Plane

Lesson 4-1

Identify Points In the diagram at the right, points are located in reference to two perpendicular number lines called **axes**. The horizontal number line is the **x-axis**, and the vertical number line is the **y-axis**. The plane containing the x- and y-axes is called the **coordinate plane**. Points in the coordinate plane are named by ordered pairs of the form (x, y). The first number, or **x-coordinate** corresponds to a number on the x-axis. The second number, or **y-coordinate**, corresponds to a number on the y-axis.

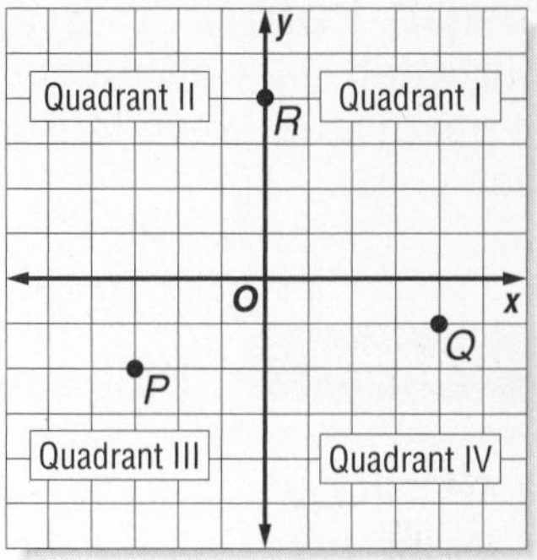

The axes divide the coordinate plane into Quadrants I, II, III, and IV, as shown. The point where the axes intersect is called the **origin**. The origin has coordinates $(0, 0)$.

Example 1 Write an ordered pair for point *R* above.

The x-coordinate is 0 and the y-coordinate is 4. Thus the ordered pair for R is $(0, 4)$.

Example 2 Write ordered pairs for points *P* and *Q* above. Then name the quadrant in which each point is located.

The x-coordinate of P is −3 and the y-coordinate is −2. Thus the ordered pair for P is $(−3, −2)$. P is in Quadrant III.

The x-coordinate of Q is 4 and the y-coordinate is −1. Thus the ordered pair for Q is $(4, −1)$. Q is in Quadrant IV.

Exercises

Write the ordered pair for each point shown at the right. Name the quadrant in which the point is located.

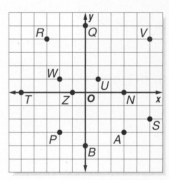

1. N

2. P

3. Q

4. R

5. S

6. T

7. U

8. V

9. W

10. Z

11. A

12. B

13. Write the ordered pair that describes a point 4 units down from and 3 units to the right of the origin.

14. Write the ordered pair that is 8 units to the left of the origin and lies on the x-axis.

4-1 **Study Guide and Intervention** *(continued)*

The Coordinate Plane

Graph Points To **graph** an ordered pair means to draw a dot at the point on the coordinate plane that corresponds to the ordered pair. To graph an ordered pair (x, y), begin at the origin. Move left or right x units. From there, move up or down y units. Draw a dot at that point.

Example **Plot each point on a coordinate plane.**

a. $R(-3, 2)$

Start at the origin. Move left 3 units since the x-coordinate is -3. Move up 2 units since the y-coordinate is 2. Draw a dot and label it R.

b. $S(0, -3)$

Start at the origin. Since the x-coordinate is 0, the point will be located on the y-axis. Move down 3 units since the y-coordinate is -3. Draw a dot and label it S.

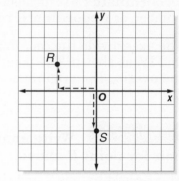

Exercises

Plot each point on the coordinate plane at the right.

1. $A(2, 4)$ **2.** $B(0, -3)$

3. $C(-4, -4)$ **4.** $D(-2, 0)$

5. $E(1, -4)$ **6.** $F(0, 0)$

7. $G(5, 0)$ **8.** $H(-3, 4)$

9. $I(4, -5)$ **10.** $J(-2, -2)$

11. $K(2, -1)$ **12.** $L(-1, -2)$

13. $M(0, 3)$ **14.** $N(5, -3)$

15. $P(4, 5)$ **16.** $Q(-5, 2)$

4-1 Skills Practice

The Coordinate Plane

Write the ordered pair for each point shown at the right. Name the quadrant in which the point is located.

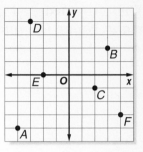

1. *A*

2. *B*

3. *C*

4. *D*

5. *E*

6. *F*

Write the ordered pair for each point shown at the right. Name the quadrant in which the point is located.

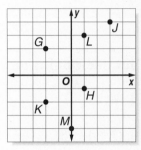

7. *G*

8. *H*

9. *J*

10. *K*

11. *L*

12. *M*

Plot each point on the coordinate plane at the right.

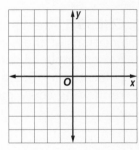

13. *M*(2, 4)

14. *N*(−3, −3)

15. *P*(2, −2)

16. *Q*(0, 3)

17. *R*(4, 1)

18. *S*(−4, 1)

Plot each point on the coordinate plane at the right.

19. *T*(4, 0)

20. *U*(−3, 2)

21. *W*(−2, −3)

22. *X*(2, 2)

23. *Y*(−3, −2)

24. *Z*(3, −3)

4-1 Practice

The Coordinate Plane

Write the ordered pair for each point shown at the right. Name the quadrant in which the point is located.

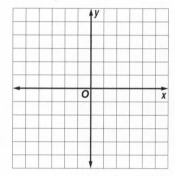

1. *A*   2. *B*

3. *C*   4. *D*

5. *E*   6. *F*

7. *G*   8. *H*

9. *I*   10. *J*

11. *K*   12. *L*

Plot each point on the coordinate plane at the right.

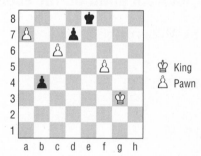

13. $M(-3, 3)$ 14. $N(3, -2)$ 15. $P(5, 1)$

16. $Q(-4, -3)$ 17. $R(0, 5)$ 18. $S(-1, -2)$

19. $T(-5, 1)$ 20. $V(1, -5)$ 21. $W(2, 0)$

22. $X(-2, -4)$ 23. $Y(4, 4)$ 24. $Z(-1, 2)$

25. **CHESS** Letters and numbers are used to show the positions of chess pieces and to describe their moves. For example, in the diagram at the right, a white pawn is located at f5. Name the positions of each of the remaining chess pieces.

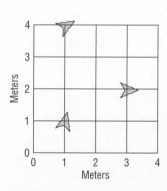

ARCHAEOLOGY For Exercises 26 and 27, use the grid at the right that shows the location of arrowheads excavated at a *midden*—a place where people in the past dumped trash, food remains, and other discarded items.

26. Write the coordinates of each arrowhead.

27. Suppose an archaeologist discovers two other arrowheads located at (1, 2) and (3, 3). Draw an arrowhead at each of these locations on the grid.

4-1 Reading to Learn Mathematics

The Coordinate Plane

Pre-Activity **How do archaeologists use coordinate systems?**

Read the introduction to Lesson 4-1 at the top of page 192 in your textbook.

What do the terms *grid system*, *grid*, and *coordinate system* mean to you?

Reading the Lesson

1. Use the coordinate plane shown at the right.

  a. Label the origin *O*.

  b. Label the *y*-axis *y*.

  c. Label the *x*-axis *x*.

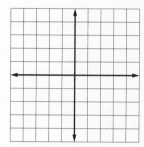

2. Explain why the coordinates of the origin are (0, 0).

3. Use the ordered pair (−2, 3).

  a. Explain how to identify the *x*- and *y*-coordinates.

  b. Name the *x*- and *y*-coordinates.

  c. Describe the steps you would use to locate the point for (−2, 3) on the coordinate plane.

4. What does the term *quadrant* mean?

Helping You Remember

5. Explain how the way the axes are labeled on the coordinate plane can help you remember how to plot the point for an ordered pair.

217

Lesson 4-1

4-1 **Enrichment**

Midpoint

The *midpoint* of a line segment is the point that lies exactly halfway between the two endpoints of the segment. The coordinates of the midpoint of a line segment whose endpoints are (x_1, y_1) and (x_2, y_2) are given by $\left(\dfrac{x_1 + x_2}{2}, \dfrac{y_1 + y_2}{2} \right)$.

Find the midpoint of each line segment with the given endpoints.

1. $(7, 1)$ and $(-3, 1)$

2. $(5, -2)$ and $(9, -8)$

3. $(-4, 4)$ and $(4, -4)$

4. $(-3, -6)$ and $(-10, -15)$

Plot each segment in the coordinate plane. Then find the coordinates of the midpoint.

5. $\overline{JK}$ with $J(5, 2)$ and $K(-2, -4)$

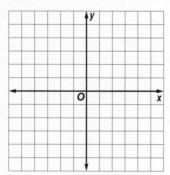

6. $\overline{PQ}$ with $P(-1, 4)$ and $Q(3, -1)$

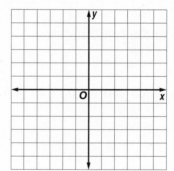

You are given the coordinates of one endpoint of a line segment and the midpoint M. Find the coordinates of the other endpoint.

7. $A(-10, 3)$ and $M(-6, 7)$

8. $D(-1, 4)$ and $M(3, -6)$

4-2 Study Guide and Intervention

Transformations on the Coordinate Plane

Transform Figures **Transformations** are movements of geometric figures. The **preimage** is the position of the figure before the transformation, and the **image** is the position of the figure after the transformation.

Reflection	A figure is flipped over a line.
Translation	A figure is slid horizontally, vertically, or both.
Dilation	A figure is enlarged or reduced.
Rotation	A figure is turned around a point.

Example Determine whether each transformation is a *reflection, translation, dilation*, or *rotation*.

a.   The figure has been flipped over a line, so this is a reflection.

b.   The figure has been turned around a point, so this is a rotation.

c.   The figure has been reduced in size, so this is a dilation.

d.    The figure has been shifted horizontally to the right, so this is a translation.

Exercises

Determine whether each transformation is a *reflection, translation, dilation*, or *rotation*.

1.

2.

3.

4.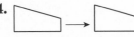

5.

6.

Lesson 4-2

4-2 Study Guide and Intervention *(continued)*

Transformations on the Coordinate Plane

Transform Figures on the Coordinate Plane You can perform transformations on a coordinate plane by changing the coordinates of each vertex. The vertices of the image of the transformed figure are indicated by the symbol ′, which is read *prime*.

Reflection over *x*-axis	$(x, y) \rightarrow (x, -y)$
Reflection over *y*-axis	$(x, y) \rightarrow (-x, y)$
Translation	$(x, y) \rightarrow (x + a, y + b)$
Dilation	$(x, y) \rightarrow (kx, ky)$
Rotation 90° counterclockwise	$(x, y) \rightarrow (-y, x)$
Rotation 180°	$(x, y) \rightarrow (-x, -y)$

Example A triangle has vertices $A(-1, 1)$, $B(2, 4)$, and $C(3, 0)$. Find the coordinates of the vertices of each image below.

a. reflection over the *x*-axis

To reflect a point over the *x*-axis, multiply the *y*-coordinate by -1.

$A(-1, 1) \rightarrow A'(-1, -1)$
$B(2, 4) \rightarrow B'(2, -4)$
$C(3, 0) \rightarrow C'(3, 0)$

The coordinates of the image vertices are $A'(-1, -1)$, $B'(2, -4)$, and $C'(3, 0)$.

b. dilation with a scale factor of 2

Find the coordinates of the dilated figure by multiplying the coordinates by 2.

$A(-1, 1) \rightarrow A'(-2, 2)$
$B(2, 4) \rightarrow B'(4, 8)$
$C(3, 0) \rightarrow C'(6, 0)$

The coordinates of the image vertices are $A'(-2, 2)$, $B'(4, 8)$, and $C'(6, 0)$.

Exercises

Find the coordinates of the vertices of each figure after the given transformation is performed.

1. triangle *RST* with $R(-2, 4)$, $S(2, 0)$, $T(-1, -1)$ reflected over the *y*-axis

2. triangle *ABC* with $A(0, 0)$, $B(2, 4)$, $C(3, 0)$ rotated about the origin 180°

3. parallelogram *ABCD* with $A(-3, 0)$, $B(-2, 3)$, $C(3, 3)$, $D(2, 0)$ translated 3 units down

4. quadrilateral *RSTU* with $R(-2, 2)$, $S(2, 4)$, $T(4, 4)$, $U(4, 0)$ dilated by a factor of $\frac{1}{2}$

5. triangle *ABC* with $A(-4, 0)$, $B(-2, 3)$, $C(0, 0)$ rotated counterclockwise 90°

6. hexagon *ABCDEF* with $A(0, 0)$, $B(-2, 3)$, $C(0, 4)$, $D(3, 4)$, $E(4, 2)$, $F(3, 0)$ translated 2 units up and 1 unit to the left

4-2 Skills Practice

Transformations on the Coordinate Plane

Identify each transformation as a *reflection*, *translation*, *dilation*, or *rotation*.

1.

2.

3.

4.

5.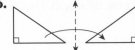

6.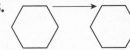

For Exercises 7–10, complete parts a and b.

a. Find the coordinates of the vertices of each figure after the given transformation is performed.

b. Graph the preimage and its image.

7. triangle *ABC* with *A*(1, 2), *B*(4, −1), and *C*(1, −1) reflected over the *y*-axis

8. parallelogram *PQRS* with *P*(−2, −1), *Q*(3, −1), *R*(2, −3), and *S*(−3, −3) translated 3 units up

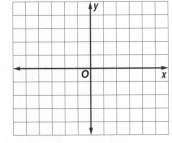

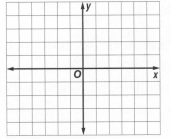

9. trapezoid *JKLM* with *J*(−2, 1), *K*(2, 1), *L*(1, −1), and *M*(−1, −1) dilated by a scale factor of 2

10. triangle *STU* with *S*(3, 3), *T*(5, 1), and *U*(1, 1) rotated 90° counterclockwise about the origin

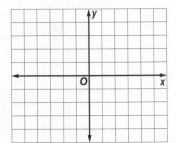

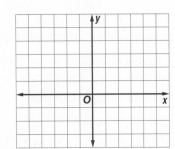

Glencoe Algebra 1

Lesson 4-2

4-2 Practice

Transformations on the Coordinate Plane

Identify each transformation as a *reflection, translation, dilation,* or *rotation*.

1.

2.

3.

For Exercises 4–6, complete parts a and b.

a. Find the coordinates of the vertices of each figure after the given transformation is performed.

b. Graph the preimage and its image.

4. triangle *DEF* with *D*(2, 3),
   E(4, 1), and *F*(1, −1)
   translated 4 units left
   and 3 units down

5. trapezoid *EFGH* with
   E(3, 2), *F*(3, −3),
   G(1, −2), and *H*(1, 1)
   reflected over the *y*-axis

6. triangle *XYZ* with *X*(3, 1),
   Y(4, −2), and *Z*(1, −3)
   rotated 90° counterclockwise
   about the origin

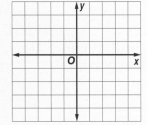

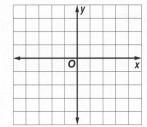

GRAPHICS For Exercises 7–9, use the diagram at the right and the following information.

A designer wants to dilate the rocket by a scale factor of $\frac{1}{2}$, and then translate it $5\frac{1}{2}$ units up.

7. Write the coordinates for the vertices of the rocket.

8. Find the coordinates of the final position of the rocket.

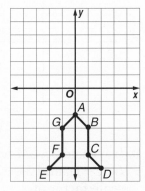

9. Graph the image on the coordinate plane.

10. **DESIGN** Ramona transformed figure *ABCDEF* to design a
    pattern for a quilt. Name two different sets of transformations
    she could have used to design the pattern.

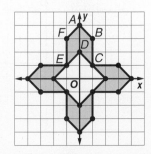

4-2 **Reading to Learn Mathematics**

Transformations on the Coordinate Plane

Pre-Activity **How are transformations used in computer graphics?**

Read the introduction to Lesson 4-2 at the top of page 197 in your textbook.

In the sentence, "Computer graphic designers can create movement that mimics real-life situations," what phrase indicates the use of transformations?

_____

Reading the Lesson

1. Suppose you look at a diagram that shows two figures *ABCDE* and *A'B'C'D'E'*. If one figure was obtained from the other by using a transformation, how do you tell which was the original figure?

_____

_____

2. Write the letter of the term and the Roman numeral of the figure that best matches each statement.

   a. A figure is flipped over a line. _____   **A.** dilation   **I.**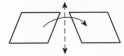

   b. A figure is turned around a point. _____   **B.** translation   **II.**

   c. A figure is enlarged or reduced. _____   **C.** reflection   **III.**

   d. A figure is slid horizontally, vertically, or both. _____   **D.** rotation   **IV.**

Helping You Remember

3. Give examples of things in everyday life that can help you remember what reflections, dilations, and rotations are.

_____

4-2 Enrichment

The Legendary City of Ur

The city of Ur was founded more than five thousand years ago in Mesopotamia (modern-day Iraq). It was one of the world's first cities. Between 1922 and 1934, archeologists discovered many treasures from this ancient city. A large cemetery from the 26th century B.C. was found to contain large quantities of gold, silver, bronze, and jewels. The many cultural artifacts that were found, such as musical instruments, weapons, mosaics, and statues, have provided historians with valuable clues about the civilization that existed in early Mesopotamia.

1. Suppose that the ordered pairs below represent the volume (cm^3) and mass (grams) of ten artifacts from the city of Ur. Plot each point on the graph.

   $A(10, 150)$

   $B(150, 1350)$

   $C(200, 1760)$

   $D(50, 525)$

   $E(100, 1500)$

   $F(10, 88)$

   $G(200, 2100)$

   $H(150, 1675)$

   $I(100, 900)$

   $J(50, 440)$

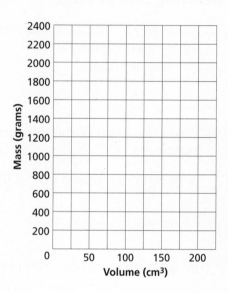

2. The equation relating mass, density, and volume for silver is $m = 10.5V$. Which of the points in Exercise 1 are solutions for this equation?

3. Suppose that the equation $m = 8.8V$ relates mass, density, and volume for the kind of bronze used in the ancient city of Ur. Which of the points in Exercise 1 are solutions for this equation?

4. Explain why the graph in Exercise 1 shows only quadrant 1.

4-3 Study Guide and Intervention

Relations

Represent Relations A **relation** is a set of ordered pairs. A relation can be represented by a set of ordered pairs, a table, a graph, or a **mapping**. A mapping illustrates how each element of the domain is paired with an element in the range.

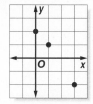 **Example 1** Express the relation {(1, 1), (0, 2), (3, −2)} as a table, a graph, and a mapping. State the domain and range of the relation.

x	y
1	1
0	2
3	−2

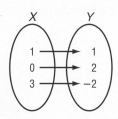

The domain for this relation is {0, 1, 3}.
The range for this relation is {−2, 1, 2}.

Example 2 A person playing racquetball uses 4 calories per hour for every pound he or she weighs.

a. Make a table to show the relation between weight and calories burned in one hour for people weighing 100, 110, 120, and 130 pounds.
Source: *The Math Teacher's Book of Lists*

x	y
100	400
110	440
120	480
130	520

b. Give the domain and range.
domain: {100, 110, 120, 130}
range: {400, 440, 480, 520}

c. Graph the relation.

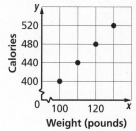

Exercises

1. Express the relation {(−2, −1), (3, 3), (4, 3)} as a table, a graph, and a mapping. Then determine the domain and range.

x	y

2. The temperature in a house drops 2° for every hour the air conditioner is on between the hours of 6 A.M. and 11 A.M. Make a graph to show the relationship between time and temperature if the temperature at 6 A.M. was 82°F.

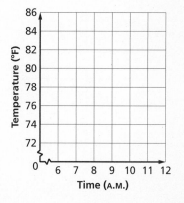

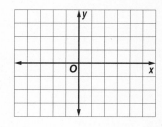

Lesson 4-3

4-3 **Study Guide and Intervention** *(continued)*

Relations

Inverse Relations The **inverse** of any relation is obtained by switching the coordinates in each ordered pair.

Example Express the relation shown in the mapping as a set of ordered pairs. Then write the inverse of the relation.

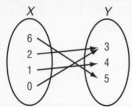

Relation: $\{(6, 5), (2, 3), (1, 4), (0, 3)\}$
Inverse: $\{(5, 6), (3, 2), (4, 1), (3, 0)\}$

Exercises

Express the relation shown in each table, mapping, or graph as a set of ordered pairs. Then write the inverse of each relation.

1.

x	y
−2	4
−1	3
2	1
4	5

2.

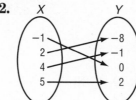

3.

x	y
−3	5
−2	−1
1	0
2	4

4.

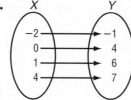

5.

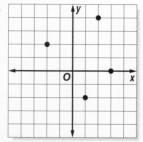

6.

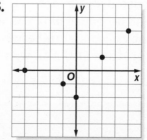

Glencoe Algebra 1

4-3 Skills Practice

Relations

Express each relation as a table, a graph, and a mapping. Then determine the domain and range.

1. {(−1, −1), (1, 1), (2, 1), (3, 2)}

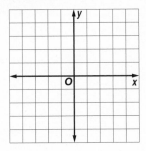

2. {(0, 4), (−4, −4), (−2, 3), (4, 0)}

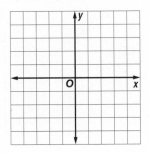

3. {(3, −2), (1, 0), (−2, 4), (3, 1)}

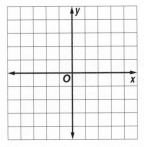

Express the relation shown in each table, mapping, or graph as a set of ordered pairs. Then write the inverse of the relation.

4.

x	y
3	−5
−4	3
7	6
1	−2

5.

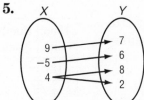

6.

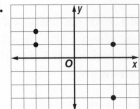

Glencoe Algebra 1

4-3 Practice

Relations

Express each relation as a table, a graph, and a mapping. Then determine the domain and range.

1. {(4, 3), (−1, 4), (3, −2), (2, 3), (−2, 1)}

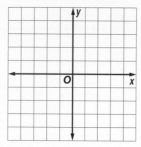

Express the relation shown in each table, mapping, or graph as a set of ordered pairs. Then write the inverse of the relation.

2.

x	y
0	9
−8	3
2	−6
1	4

3.

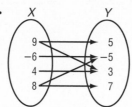

4.

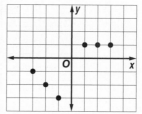

BASEBALL For Exercises 5 and 6, use the graph that shows the batting average for Barry Bonds of the San Francisco Giants. **Source:** www.sportsillustrated.cnn.com

5. Find the domain and estimate the range.

6. Which seasons did Bonds have the lowest and highest batting averages?

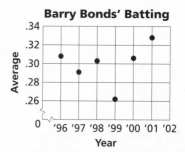

METEORS For Exercises 7 and 8, use the table that shows the number of meteors Ann observed each hour during a meteor shower.

Time (A.M.)	Number of Meteors
12	15
1	26
2	28
3	28
4	15

7. What are the domain and range?

8. Graph the relation.

4-3 **Reading to Learn Mathematics**
Relations

Pre-Activity **How can relations be used to represent baseball statistics?**

Read the introduction to Lesson 4-3 at the top of page 205 in your textbook.

In 1997, Ken Griffey, Jr. had _____ home runs and _____ strikeouts.

This can be represented with the ordered pair (_____, _____).

Reading the Lesson

1. Look at page 205 in your textbook. There you see the same relation represented by a set of ordered pairs, a table, a graph, and a mapping.

   a. In the list of ordered pairs, where do you see the numbers for the domain? the numbers for the range?

   b. What parts of the table show the domain and the range?

   c. How do the table, the graph, and the mapping show that there are three ordered pairs in the relation?

2. Which tells you more about a relation, a list of the ordered pairs in the relation or the domain and range of the relation? Explain.

3. Describe how you would find the inverse of the relation {(1, 2), (2, 4), (3, 6), (4, 8)}.

Helping You Remember

4. The first letters in two words and their order in the alphabet can sometimes help you remember their mathematical meaning. Two key terms in this lesson are *domain* and *range*. Describe how the alphabet method could help you remember their meaning.

Lesson 4-3

4-3 Enrichment

Inverse Relations

On each grid below, plot the points in Sets A and B. Then connect the
points in Set A with the corresponding points in Set B. Then find the
inverses of Set A and Set B, plot the two sets, and connect those points.

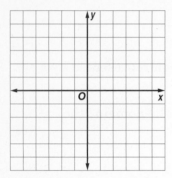

Set A	Set B
$(-4, 0)$	$(0, 1)$
$(-3, 0)$	$(0, 2)$
$(-2, 0)$	$(0, 3)$
$(-1, 0)$	$(0, 4)$

Inverse

	Set A	Set B
1.	_____	
2.	_____	
3.	_____	
4.	_____	

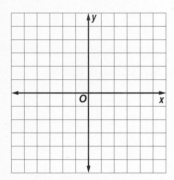

Set A	Set B
$(-3, -3)$	$(-2, 1)$
$(-2, -2)$	$(-1, 2)$
$(-1, -1)$	$(0, 3)$
$(0, 0)$	$(1, 4)$

Inverse

	Set A	Set B
5.	_____	
6.	_____	
7.	_____	
8.	_____	

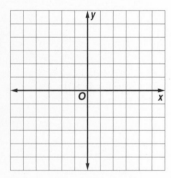

Set A	Set B
$(-4, 1)$	$(3, 2)$
$(-3, 2)$	$(3, 2)$
$(-2, 3)$	$(3, 2)$
$(-1, 4)$	$(3, 2)$

Inverse

	Set A	Set B
9.	_____	
10.	_____	
11.	_____	
12.	_____	

13. What is the graphical relationship between the line segments you drew
connecting points in Sets A and B and the line segments connecting points
in the inverses of those two sets?

4-4 Study Guide and Intervention

Equations as Relations

Solve Equations The equation $y = 3x - 4$ is an example of an **equation in two variables** because it contains two variables, x and y. The **solution** of an equation in two variables is an ordered pair of replacements for the variables that results in a true statement when substituted into the equation.

Example 1 Find the solution set for $y = -2x - 1$, given the replacement set $\{(-2, 3), (0, -1), (1, -2), (3, 1)\}$.

Make a table. Substitute the x and y-values of each ordered pair into the equation.

x	y	y = −2x − 1	True or False
−2	3	3 = −2(−2) − 1 3 = 3	True
0	−1	−1 = −2(0) − 1 −1 = −1	True
1	−2	−2 = −2(1) − 1 −2 = −3	False
3	1	1 = −2(3) − 1 1 = −7	False

The ordered pairs $(-2, 3)$, and $(0, -1)$ result in true statements. The solution set is $\{(-2, 3), (0, -1)\}$.

Example 2 Solve $b = 2a - 1$ if the domain is $\{-2, -1, 0, 2, 4\}$.

Make a table. The values of a come from the domain. Substitute each value of a into the equation to determine the corresponding values of b in the range.

a	2a − 1	b	(a, b)
−2	2(−2) − 1	−5	(−2, −5)
−1	2(−1) − 1	−3	(−1, −3)
0	2(0) − 1	−1	(0, −1)
2	2(2) − 1	3	(2, 3)
4	2(4) − 1	7	(4, 7)

The solution set is $\{(-2, -5), (-1, -3), (0, -1), (2, 3), (4, 7)\}$.

Exercises

Find the solution set of each equation, given the replacement set.

1. $y = 3x + 1$; $\{(0, 1), \left(\frac{1}{3}, 2\right), \left(-1, -\frac{2}{3}\right), (-1, -2)\}$

2. $3x - 2y = 6$; $\{(-2, 3), (0, 1), (0, -3), (2, 0)\}$

3. $2x = 5 - y$; $\{(1, 3), (2, 1), (3, 2), (4, 3)\}$

Solve each equation if the domain is $(-4, -2, 0, 2, 4\}$.

4. $x + y = 4$

5. $y = -4x - 6$

6. $5a - 2b = 10$

7. $3x - 2y = 12$

8. $6x + 3y = 18$

9. $4x + 8 = 2y$

10. $x - y = 8$

11. $2x + y = 10$

Lesson 4-4

4-4 **Study Guide and Intervention** (continued)

Equations as Relations

Graph Solution Sets You can graph the ordered pairs in the solution set of an equation in two variables. The domain contains values represented by the **independent variable**. The range contains the corresponding values represented by the **dependent variable**, which are determined by the given equation.

Example **Solve $4x + 2y = 12$ if the domain is $(-1, 0, 2, 4)$. Graph the solution set.**

First solve the equation for y in terms of x.

$$4x + 2y = 12 \qquad \text{Original equation}$$
$$4x + 2y - 4x = 12 - 4x \qquad \text{Subtract } 4x \text{ from each side.}$$
$$2y = 12 - 4x \qquad \text{Simplify.}$$
$$\frac{2y}{2} = \frac{12 - 4x}{2} \qquad \text{Divide each side by 2.}$$
$$y = 6 - 2x \qquad \text{Simplify.}$$

Substitute each value of x from the domain to determine the corresponding value of y in the range.

x	$6 - 2x$	y	(x, y)
-1	$6 - 2(-1)$	8	$(-1, 8)$
0	$6 - 2(0)$	6	$(0, 6)$
2	$6 - 2(2)$	2	$(2, 2)$
4	$6 - 2(4)$	-2	$(4, -2)$

Graph the solution set.

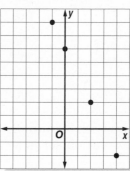

Exercises

Solve each equation for the given domain. Graph the solution set.

1. $x + 2y = 4$ for $x = \{-2, 0, 2, 4\}$

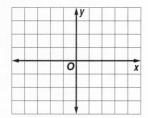

2. $y = -2x - 3$ for $x = \{-2, -1, 0, 1\}$

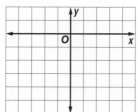

3. $x - 3y = 6$ for $x = \{-3, 0, 3, 6\}$

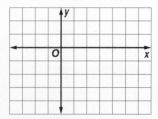

4. $2x - 4y = 8$ for $x = \{-4, -2, 0, 2\}$

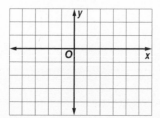

Glencoe Algebra 1

4-4 Skills Practice

Equations as Relations

Find the solution set for each equation, given the replacement set.

1. $y = 3x - 1$; $\{(2, 5), (-2, 7), (0, -1), (1, 1)\}$

2. $y = 2x + 4$; $\{(-1, -2), (-3, 2), (1, 6), (-2, 8)\}$

3. $y = 7 - 2x$; $\{(3, 1), (4, -1), (5, -3), (-1, 5)\}$

4. $-3x + y = 2$; $\{(-3, 7), (-2, -4), (-1, -1), (3, 11)\}$

Solve each equation if the domain is $\{-2, -1, 0, 2, 5\}$.

5. $y = x + 4$

6. $y = 3x - 2$

7. $y = 2x + 1$

8. $x = y + 2$

9. $x = 3 - y$

10. $2x + y = 4$

11. $2x - y = 7$

12. $4x + 2y = 6$

Solve each equation for the given domain. Graph the solution set.

13. $y = 2x + 5$ for $x = \{-5, -4, -2, -1, 0\}$

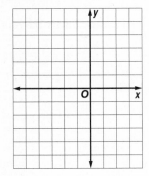

14. $y = 2x - 3$ for $x = \{-1, 1, 2, 3, 4\}$

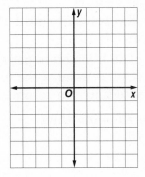

15. $2x + y = 1$ for $x = \{-2, -1, 0, 2, 3\}$

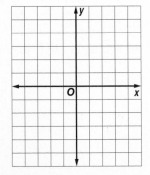

16. $2x - 2y = 6$ for $x = \{-3, -1, 3, 4, 6\}$

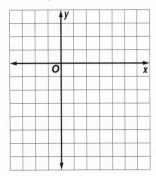

Glencoe Algebra 1

Lesson 4-4

4-4 Practice

Equations as Relations

Find the solution set for each equation, given the replacement set.

1. $y = 2 - 5x$; $\{(3, 12), (-3, -17), (2, -8), (-1, 7)\}$

2. $3x - 2y = -1$; $\{(-1, 1), (-2, -2.5), (-1, -1.5), (0, 0.5)\}$

Solve each equation if the domain is $\{-2, -1, 2, 3, 5\}$.

3. $y = 4 - 2x$

4. $x = 8 - y$

5. $4x + 2y = 10$

6. $3x - 6y = 12$

7. $2x + 4y = 16$

8. $x - \frac{1}{2}y = 6$

Solve each equation for the given domain. Graph the solution set.

9. $2x - 4y = 8$ for $x = \{-4, -3, -2, 2, 5\}$ **10.** $\frac{1}{2}x + y = 1$ for $x = \{-4, -3, -2, 0, 4\}$

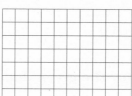

EARTH SCIENCE **For Exercises 11 and 12, use the following information.**

Earth moves at a rate of 30 kilometers per second around the Sun. The equation $d = 30t$ relates the distance d in kilometers Earth moves to time t in seconds.

11. Find the set of ordered pairs when $t = \{10, 20, 30, 45, 70\}$.

12. Graph the set of ordered pairs.

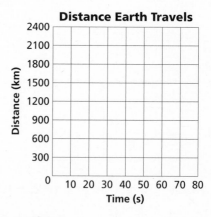

Distance Earth Travels

GEOMETRY **For Exercises 13–15, use the following information.**

The equation for the area of a triangle is $A = \frac{1}{2}bh$. Suppose the area of triangle DEF is 30 square inches.

13. Solve the equation for h.

14. State the independent and dependent variables.

15. Choose 5 values for b and find the corresponding values for h.

4-4 Reading to Learn Mathematics

Equations as Relations

Pre-Activity **Why are equations of relations important in traveling?**

Read the introduction to Lesson 4-4 at the top of page 212 in your textbook.

• In the equation $p = 0.69d$, p represents _____ and d

  represents _____.

• How many variables are in the equation $p = 0.69d$?

Reading the Lesson

1. Suppose you make the following table to solve an equation that uses the domain $\{-3, -2, -1, 0, 1\}$.

x	x − 4	y	(x, y)
−3	−3 − 4	−7	(−3, −7)
−2	−2 − 4	−6	(−2, −6)
−1	−1 − 4	−5	(−1, −5)
0	0 − 4	−4	(0, −4)
1	1 − 4	−3	(1, −3)

a. What is the equation?

b. Which column shows the *domain*?

c. Which column shows the *range*?

d. Which column shows the *solution set*?

2. The solution set of the equation $y = 2x$ for a given domain is $\{(-2, -4), (0, 0), (2, 4), (7, 14)\}$. Tell whether each sentence is *true* or *false*. If false, replace the underlined word(s) to make a true sentence.

a. The domain contains the values represented by the <u>independent variable</u>.

b. The <u>domain</u> contains the numbers −4, 0, 4, and 14.

c. For each number in the domain, the range contains a corresponding number that is a value of the <u>dependent variable</u>.

3. What is meant by "solving an equation for y in terms of x"?

Helping You Remember

4. Remember, *when you solve an equation for a given variable, that variable becomes the dependent variable*. Write an equation and describe how you would identify the dependent variable.

Lesson 4-4

4-4 Enrichment

Coordinate Geometry and Area

How would you find the area of a triangle whose vertices have the coordinates $A(-1, 2)$, $B(1, 4)$, and $C(3, 0)$?

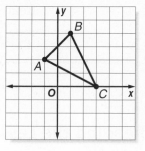

When a figure has no sides parallel to either axis, the height and base are difficult to find.

One method of finding the area is to enclose the figure in a rectangle and subtract the area of the surrounding triangles from the area of the rectangle.

Area of rectangle $DEFC$

$= 4 \times 4$

$= 16$ square units

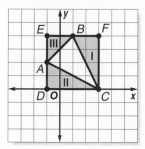

Area of triangle I $= \frac{1}{2}(2)(4) = 4$

Area of triangle II $= \frac{1}{2}(2)(4) = 4$

Area of triangle III $= \frac{1}{2}(2)(2) = 2$

Total $= 10$ square units

Area of triangle $ABC = 16 - 10$, or 6 square units

Find the areas of the figures with the following vertices.

1. $A(-4, -6)$, $B(0, 4)$, $C(4, 2)$

2. $A(6, -2)$, $B(8, -10)$, $C(12, -6)$

3. $A(0, 2)$, $B(2, 7)$, $C(6, 10)$, $D(9, -2)$

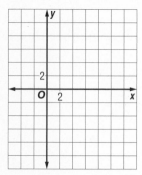

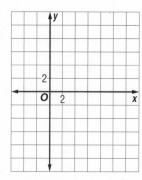

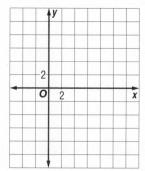

4-5 Study Guide and Intervention

Graphing Linear Equations

Identify Linear Equations A **linear equation** is an equation that can be written in the form $Ax + By = C$. This is called the **standard form** of a linear equation.

Standard Form of a Linear Equation	$Ax + By = C$, where $A \geq 0$, A and B are not both zero, and A, B, and C are integers whose GCF is 1.

Example 1 Determine whether $y = 6 - 3x$ is a linear equation. If so, write the equation in standard form.

First rewrite the equation so both variables are on the same side of the equation.

$y = 6 - 3x$ Original equation
$y + 3x = 6 - 3x + 3x$ Add 3x to each side.
$3x + y = 6$ Simplify.

The equation is now in standard form, with $A = 3$, $B = 1$ and $C = 6$. This is a linear equation.

Example 2 Determine whether $3xy + y = 4 + 2x$ is a linear equation. If so, write the equation in standard form.

Since the term $3xy$ has two variables, the equation cannot be written in the form $Ax + By = C$. Therefore, this is not a linear equation.

Exercises

Determine whether each equation is a linear equation. If so, write the equation in standard form.

1. $2x = 4y$

2. $6 + y = 8$

3. $4x - 2y = -1$

4. $3xy + 8 = 4y$

5. $3x - 4 = 12$

6. $y = x^2 + 7$

7. $y - 4x = 9$

8. $x + 8 = 0$

9. $-2x + 3 = 4y$

10. $2 + \frac{1}{2}x = y$

11. $\frac{1}{4}y = 12 - 4x$

12. $3xy - y = 8$

13. $6x + 4y - 3 = 0$

14. $yx - 2 = 8$

15. $6a - 2b = 8 + b$

16. $\frac{1}{4}x - 12y = 1$

17. $3 + x + x^2 = 0$

18. $x^2 = 2xy$

Lesson 4-5

4-5 ## Study Guide and Intervention *(continued)*

Graphing Linear Equations

Graph Linear Equations The graph of a linear equation is a line. The line represents all solutions to the linear equation. Also, every ordered pair on this line satisfies the equation.

Example **Graph the equation $y - 2x = 1$.**

Solve the equation for y.

$$y - 2x = 1$$ Original equation
$$y - 2x + 2x = 1 + 2x$$ Add $2x$ to each side.
$$y = 2x + 1$$ Simplify.

Select five values for the domain and make a table. Then graph the ordered pairs and draw a line through the points.

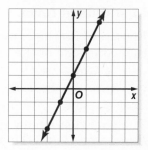

x	2x + 1	y	(x, y)
−2	2(−2) + 1	−3	(−2, −3)
−1	2(−1) + 1	−1	(−1, −1)
0	2(0) + 1	1	(0, 1)
1	2(1) + 1	3	(1, 3)
2	2(2) + 1	5	(2, 5)

Exercises

Graph each equation.

1. $y = 4$

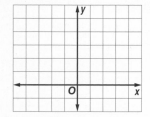

2. $y = 2x$

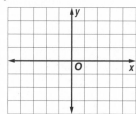

3. $x - y = -1$

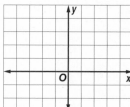

4. $3x + 2y = 6$

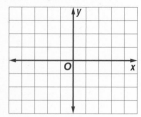

5. $x + 2y = 4$

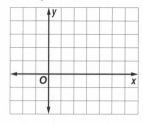

6. $2x + y = -2$

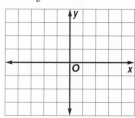

7. $3x - 6y = -3$

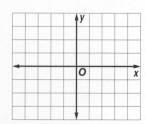

8. $-2x + y = -2$

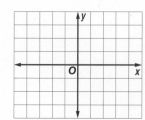

9. $\frac{1}{4}x + \frac{3}{4}y = 6$

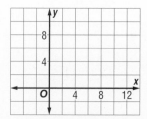

Glencoe Algebra 1

4-5 Skills Practice

Graphing Linear Equations

Determine whether each equation is a linear equation. If so, write the equation in standard form.

1. $xy = 6$

2. $y = 2 - 3x$

3. $5x = y - 4$

4. $y = 2x + 5$

5. $y = -7 + 6x$

6. $y = 3x^2 + 1$

7. $y - 4 = 0$

8. $5x + 6y = 3x + 2$

9. $\frac{1}{2}y = 1$

Graph each equation.

10. $y = 4$

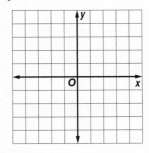

11. $y = 3x$

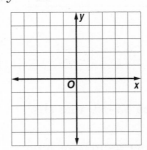

12. $y = x + 4$

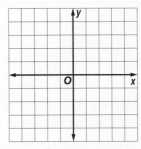

13. $y = x - 2$

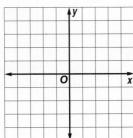

14. $y = 4 - x$

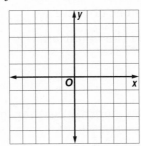

15. $y = 4 - 2x$

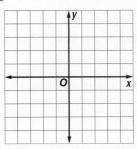

16. $x - y = 3$

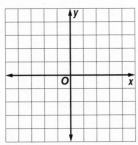

17. $10x = -5y$

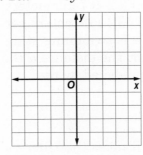

18. $4x = 2y + 6$

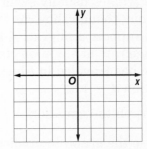

Lesson 4-5

4-5 Practice

Graphing Linear Equations

Determine whether each equation is a linear equation. If so, write the equation in standard form.

1. $4xy + 2y = 9$

2. $8x - 3y = 6 - 4x$

3. $7x + y + 3 = y$

4. $5 - 2y = 3x$

5. $4y + x = 9x$

6. $a + \frac{1}{5}b = 2$

7. $6x = 2y$

8. $\frac{x}{4} - \frac{y}{3} = 1$

9. $\frac{5}{x} - \frac{2}{y} = 7$

Graph each equation.

10. $\frac{1}{2}x - y = 2$

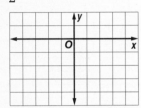

11. $5x - 2y = 7$

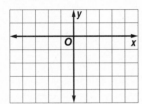

12. $1.5x + 3y = 9$

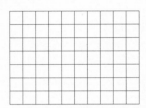

COMMUNICATIONS For Exercises 13–15, use the following information.

A telephone company charges $4.95 per month for long distance calls plus $0.05 per minute. The monthly cost c of long distance calls can be described by the equation $c = 0.05m + 4.95$, where m is the number of minutes.

13. Find the *y*-intercept of the graph of the equation.

14. Graph the equation.

15. If you talk 140 minutes, what is the monthly cost for long distance?

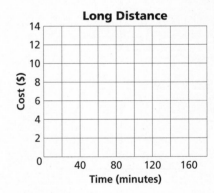

MARINE BIOLOGY For Exercises 16 and 17, use the following information.

Killer whales usually swim at a rate of 3.2–9.7 kilometers per hour, though they can travel up to 48.4 kilometers per hour. Suppose a migrating killer whale is swimming at an average rate of 4.5 kilometers per hour. The distance d the whale has traveled in t hours can be predicted by the equation $d = 4.5t$.

16. Graph the equation.

17. Use the graph to predict the time it takes the killer whale to travel 30 kilometers.

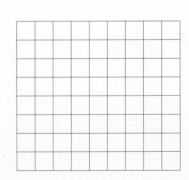

4-5 Reading to Learn Mathematics

Graphing Linear Equations

Pre-Activity **How can linear equations be used in nutrition?**

Read the introduction to Lesson 4-5 at the top of page 218 in your textbook.
In the equation $f = 0.3\left(\dfrac{C}{9}\right)$, what are the independent and dependent variables?

Reading the Lesson

1. Describe the graph of a linear equation.

2. Determine whether each equation is a linear equation. Explain.

	Equation	Linear or non-linear?	Explanation
a.	$2x = 3y + 1$		
b.	$4xy + 2y = 7$		
c.	$2x^2 = 4y - 3$		
d.	$\dfrac{x}{5} - \dfrac{4y}{3} = 2$		

3. What do the terms *x-intercept* and *y-intercept* mean?

Helping You Remember

4. Describe the method you would use to graph $4x + 2y = 8$.

Lesson 4-5

4-5 Enrichment

Taxicab Graphs

You have used a rectangular coordinate system to graph equations such as $y = x - 1$ on a coordinate plane. In a coordinate plane, the numbers in an ordered pair (x, y) can be any two real numbers.

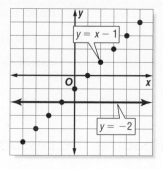

A **taxicab plane** is different from the usual coordinate plane. The only points allowed are those that exist along the horizontal and vertical grid lines. You may think of the points as taxicabs that must stay on the streets.

The taxicab graph shows the equations $y = -2$ and $y = x - 1$. Notice that one of the graphs is no longer a straight line. It is now a collection of separate points.

Graph these equations on the taxicab plane at the right.

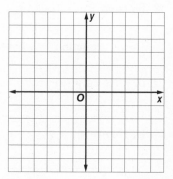

1. $y = x + 1$ **2.** $y = -2x + 3$

3. $y = 2.5$ **4.** $x = -4$

Use your graphs for these problems.

5. Which of the equations has the same graph in both the usual coordinate plane and the taxicab plane?

6. Describe the form of equations that have the same graph in both the usual coordinate plane and the taxicab plane.

In the taxicab plane, distances are not measured diagonally, but along the streets. Write the taxi-distance between each pair of points.

7. (0, 0) and (5, 2)   **8.** (0, 0) and (-3, 2)   **9.** (0, 0) and (2, 1.5)

10. (1, 2) and (4, 3)   **11.** (2, 4) and (-1, 3)   **12.** (0, 4) and (-2, 0)

Draw these graphs on the taxicab grid at the right.

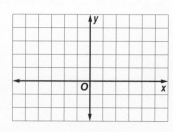

13. The set of points whose taxi-distance from (0, 0) is 2 units.

14. The set of points whose taxi-distance from (2, 1) is 3 units.

4-6 Study Guide and Intervention
Functions

Lesson 4-6

Identify Functions Relations in which each element of the domain is paired with exactly one element of the range are called **functions**.

Example 1 Determine whether the relation {(6, −3), (4, 1), (7, −2), (−3, 1)} is a function. Explain.

Since each element of the domain is paired with exactly one element of the range, this relation is a function.

Example 2 Determine whether $3x - y = 6$ is a function.

Since the equation is in the form $Ax + By = C$, the graph of the equation will be a line, as shown at the right.

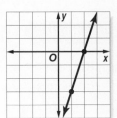

If you draw a vertical line through each value of x, the vertical line passes through just one point of the graph. Thus, the line represents a function.

Exercises

Determine whether each relation is a function.

1.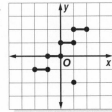

2.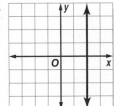

3.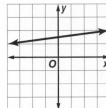

4.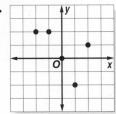

5.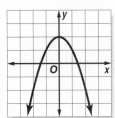

6.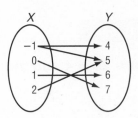

7. {(4, 2), (2, 3), (6, 1)}

8. {(−3, −3), (−3, 4), (−2, 4)}

9. {(−1, 0), (1, 0)}

10. $-2x + 4y = 0$

11. $x^2 + y^2 = 8$

12. $x = -4$

4-6 Study Guide and Intervention *(continued)*

Functions

Function Values Equations that are functions can be written in a form called **function notation**. For example, $y = 2x - 1$ can be written as $f(x) = 2x - 1$. In the function, x represents the elements of the domain, and $f(x)$ represents the elements of the range. Suppose you want to find the value in the range that corresponds to the element 2 in the domain. This is written $f(2)$ and is read "f of 2." The value of $f(2)$ is found by substituting 2 for x in the equation.

Example **If $f(x) = 3x - 4$, find each value.**

a. $f(3)$

$\begin{aligned} f(3) &= 3(3) - 4 & &\text{Replace } x \text{ with 3.} \\ &= 9 - 4 & &\text{Multiply.} \\ &= 5 & &\text{Simplify.} \end{aligned}$

b. $f(-2)$

$\begin{aligned} f(-2) &= 3(-2) - 4 & &\text{Replace } x \text{ with } -2. \\ &= -6 - 4 & &\text{Multiply.} \\ &= -10 & &\text{Simplify.} \end{aligned}$

Exercises

If $f(x) = 2x - 4$ and $g(x) = x^2 - 4x$, find each value.

1. $f(4)$

2. $g(2)$

3. $f(-5)$

4. $g(-3)$

5. $f(0)$

6. $g(0)$

7. $f(3) - 1$

8. $f\left(\dfrac{1}{4}\right)$

9. $g\left(\dfrac{1}{4}\right)$

10. $f(a^2)$

11. $f(k + 1)$

12. $g(2c)$

13. $f(3x)$

14. $f(2) + 3$

15. $g(-4)$

4-6 Skills Practice

Functions

Determine whether each relation is a function.

1.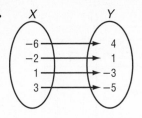

2.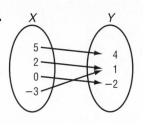

3.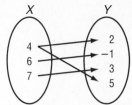

4.
x	y
4	−5
−1	−10
0	−9
1	−7
9	1

5.
x	y
2	7
5	−3
3	5
−4	−2
5	2

6.
x	y
3	7
−1	1
1	0
3	5
7	3

7. $\{(2, 5), (4, -2), (3, 3), (5, 4), (-2, 5)\}$

8. $\{(6, -1), (-4, 2), (5, 2), (4, 6), (6, 5)\}$

9. $y = 2x - 5$

10. $y = 11$

11.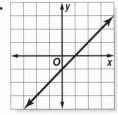

12.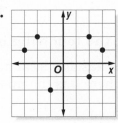

13.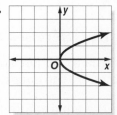

If $f(x) = 3x + 2$ and $g(x) = x^2 - x$, find each value.

14. $f(4)$

15. $f(8)$

16. $f(-2)$

17. $g(2)$

18. $g(-3)$

19. $g(-6)$

20. $f(2) + 1$

21. $f(1) - 1$

22. $g(2) - 2$

23. $g(-1) + 4$

24. $f(x + 1)$

25. $g(3b)$

4-6 Practice

Functions

Determine whether each relation is a function.

1.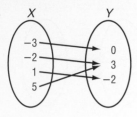

2.

x	y
1	−5
−4	3
7	6
1	−2

3.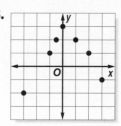

4. {(1, 4), (2, −2), (3, −6), (−6, 3), (−3, 6)}

5. {(6, −4), (2, −4), (−4, 2), (4, 6), (2, 6)}

6. $x = -2$

7. $y = 2$

If $f(x) = 2x - 6$ and $g(x) = x - 2x^2$, find each value.

8. $f(2)$

9. $f\left(-\dfrac{1}{2}\right)$

10. $g(-1)$

11. $g\left(-\dfrac{1}{3}\right)$

12. $f(7) - 9$

13. $g(-3) + 13$

14. $f(h + 9)$

15. $g(3y)$

16. $2[g(b) + 1]$

WAGES For Exercises 17 and 18, use the following information.

Martin earns $7.50 per hour proofreading ads at a local newspaper. His weekly wage w can be described by the equation $w = 7.5h$, where h is the number of hours worked.

17. Write the equation in functional notation.

18. Find $f(15)$, $f(20)$, and $f(25)$.

ELECTRICITY For Exercises 19–21, use the following information.

The table shows the relationship between resistance R and current I in a circuit.

Resistance (ohms)	120	80	48	6	4
Current (amperes)	0.1	0.15	0.25	2	3

19. Is the relationship a function? Explain.

20. If the relation can be represented by the equation $IR = 12$, rewrite the equation in functional notation so that the resistance R is a function of the current I.

21. What is the resistance in a circuit when the current is 0.5 ampere?

4-6 Reading to Learn Mathematics
Functions

Pre-Activity **How are functions used in meteorology?**

Read the introduction to Lesson 4-6 at the top of page 226 in your textbook.

If pressure is the independent variable and temperature is the dependent variable, what are the ordered pairs for this set of data?

Reading the Lesson

1. The statement, "Relations in which each element of the <u>range</u> is paired with exactly one element of the <u>domain</u> are called functions," is false. How can you change the underlined words to make the statement true?

2. Describe how each method shows that the relation represented is a function.

   a. mapping

   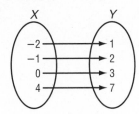

   b. vertical line test

   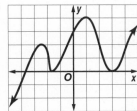

Helping You Remember

3. A student who was trying to help a friend remember how functions are different from relations that are not functions gave the following advice: *Just remember that functions are very strict and never give you a choice.* Explain how this might help you remember what a function is.

4-6 **Enrichment**

Composite Functions

Three things are needed to have a function—a set called the domain, a set called the range, and a rule that matches each element in the domain with only one element in the range. Here is an example.

Rule: $f(x) = 2x + 1$

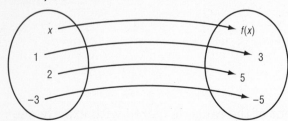

$f(x) = 2x + 1$

$f(1) = 2(1) + 1 = 2 + 1 = 3$

$f(2) = 2(2) + 1 = 4 + 1 = 5$

$f(-3) = 2(-3) + 1 = -6 + 1 = -5$

Suppose we have three sets A, B, and C and two functions described as shown below.

Rule: $f(x) = 2x + 1$ Rule: $g(y) = 3y - 4$

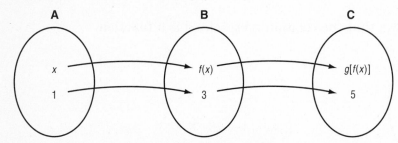

$g(y) = 3y - 4$

$g(3) = 3(3) - 4 = 5$

Let's find a rule that will match elements of set A with elements of set C without finding any elements in set B. In other words, let's find a rule for the **composite function $g[f(x)]$**.

Since $f(x) = 2x + 1, g[f(x)] = g(2x + 1)$.

Since $g(y) = 3y - 4, g(2x + 1) = 3(2x + 1) - 4$, or $6x - 1$.

Therefore, $g[f(x)] = 6x - 1$.

Find a rule for the composite function $g[f(x)]$.

1. $f(x) = 3x$ and $g(y) = 2y + 1$

2. $f(x) = x^2 + 1$ and $g(y) = 4y$

3. $f(x) = -2x$ and $g(y) = y^2 - 3y$

4. $f(x) = \dfrac{1}{x - 3}$ and $g(y) = y^{-1}$

5. Is it always the case that $g[f(x)] = f[g(x)]$? Justify your answer.

4-7 Study Guide and Intervention

Arithmetic Sequences

Recognize Arithmetic Sequences A **sequence** is a set of numbers in a specific order. If the difference between successive terms is constant, then the sequence is called an **arithmetic sequence**.

Arithmetic Sequence	a numerical pattern that increases or decreases at a constant rate or value called the **common difference**

Example 1 Determine whether the sequence 1, 3, 5, 7, 9, 11, ... is an arithmetic sequence. Justify your answer.

If possible, find the common difference between the terms. Since $3 - 1 = 2$, $5 - 3 = 2$, and so on, the common difference is 2.

Since the difference between the terms of 1, 3, 5, 7, 9, 11, ... is constant, this is an arithmetic sequence.

Example 2 Determine whether the sequence 1, 2, 4, 8, 16, 32, ... is an arithmetic sequence. Justify your answer.

If possible, find the common difference between the terms. Since $2 - 1 = 1$ and $4 - 2 = 2$, there is no common difference.

Since the difference between the terms of 1, 2, 4, 8, 16, 32, ... is not constant, this is not an arithmetic sequence.

Exercises

Determine whether each sequence is an arithmetic sequence. If it is, state the common difference.

1. 1, 5, 9, 13, 17, ...

2. 8, 4, 0, −4, −8, ...

3. 1, 3, 9, 27, 81, ...

4. 10, 15, 25, 40, 60, ...

5. −10, −5, 0, 5, 10, ...

6. 8, 6, 4, 2, 0, −2, ...

7. 4, 8, 12, 16, ...

8. 15, 12, 10, 9, ...

9. 1.1, 2.1, 3.1, 4.1, 5.1, ...

10. 8, 7, 6, 5, 4, ...

11. 0.5, 1.5, 2.5, 3.5, 4.5, ...

12. 1, 4, 16, 64, ...

13. 10, 14, 18, 22, ...

14. −3, −6, −9, −12, ...

15. 7, 0, −7, −14, ...

4-7 Study Guide and Intervention (continued)

Arithmetic Sequences

Write Arithmetic Sequences You can use the common difference of an arithmetic sequence to find the next term of the sequence. Each term after the first term is found by adding the preceding term and the common difference.

Terms of an Arithmetic Sequence	If a_1 is the first term of an arithmetic sequence with common difference d, then the sequence is a_1, $a_1 + d$, $a_1 + 2d$, $a_1 + 3d$, ...
nth Term of an Arithmetic Sequence	$a_n = a_1 + (n - 1)d$

Example 1 Find the next three terms of the arithmetic sequence 28, 32, 36, 40, ...

Find the common difference by subtracting successive terms.

28   32   36   40
  + 4   + 4   + 4

The common difference is 4.

Add 4 to the last given term, 40, to get the next term. Continue adding 4 until the next three terms are found.

40   44   48   52
  + 4   + 4   + 4

The next three terms are 44, 48, 52.

Example 2 Write an equation for the nth term of the sequence 12, 15, 18, 21, ...

In this sequence, a_1 is 12. Find the common difference.

12   15   18   21
  + 3   + 3   + 3

The common difference is 3.

Use the formula for the nth term to write an equation.

$a_n = a_1 + (n - 1)d$ Formula for the nth term
$a_n = 12 + (n - 1)3$ $a_1 = 12$, $d = 3$
$a_n = 12 + 3n - 3$ Distributive Property
$a_n = 3n + 9$ Simplify.

The equation for the nth term is $a_n = 3n + 9$.

Exercises

Find the next three terms of each arithmetic sequence.

1. 9, 13, 17, 21, 25, ...

2. 4, 0, −4, −8, −12, ...

3. 29, 35, 41, 47, ...

4. −10, −5, 0, 5, ...

5. 2.5, 5, 7.5, 10, ...

6. 3.1, 4.1, 5.1, 6.1, ...

Find the nth term of each arithmetic sequence described.

7. $a_1 = 6$, $d = 3$, $n = 10$

8. $a_1 = -2$, $d = -3$, $n = 8$

9. $a_1 = 1$, $d = -5$, $n = 20$

10. $a_1 = -3$, $d = -2$, $n = 50$

11. $a_1 = -12$, $d = 4$, $n = 20$

12. $a_1 = 1$, $d = \frac{1}{2}$, $n = 11$

Write an equation for the nth term of the arithmetic sequence.

13. 1, 3, 5, 7, ...

14. −1, −4, −7, −10, ...

15. −4, −9, −14, −19, ...

4-7 **Skills Practice**

Arithmetic Sequences

Determine whether each sequence is an arithmetic sequence. If it is, state the common difference.

1. 4, 7, 9, 12, ...

2. 15, 13, 11, 9, ...

3. 7, 10, 13, 16, ...

4. −6, −5, −3, −1, ...

5. −5, −3, −1, 1, ...

6. −9, −12, −15, −18, ...

Find the next three terms of each arithmetic sequence.

7. 3, 7, 11, 15, ...

8. 22, 20, 18, 16, ...

9. −13, −11, −9, −7, ...

10. −2, −5, −8, −11, ...

11. 19, 24, 29, 34, ...

12. 16, 7, −2, −11, ...

Find the nth term of each arithmetic sequence described.

13. $a_1 = 6, d = 3, n = 12$

14. $a_1 = -2, d = 5, n = 11$

15. $a_1 = 10, d = -3, n = 15$

16. $a_1 = -3, d = -3, n = 22$

17. $a_1 = 24, d = 8, n = 25$

18. $a_1 = 8, d = -6, n = 14$

19. 8, 13, 18, 23, ... for $n = 17$

20. −10, −3, 4, 11, ... for $n = 12$

21. 12, 10, 8, 6, ... for $n = 16$

22. 12, 7, 2, −3, ... for $n = 25$

Write an equation for the nth term of each arithmetic sequence. Then graph the first five terms of the sequence.

23. 7, 13, 19, 25, ...

24. 30, 26, 22, 18, ...

25. −7, −4, −1, 2, ...

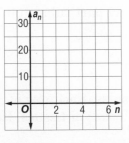

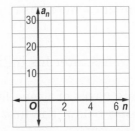

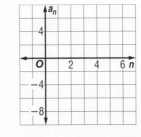

4-7 Practice

Arithmetic Sequences

Determine whether each sequence is an arithmetic sequence. If it is, state the common difference.

1. 21, 13, 5, −3, ...

2. −5, 12, 29, 46, ...

3. −2.2, −1.1, 0.1, 1.3, ...

Find the next three terms of each arithmetic sequence.

4. 82, 76, 70, 64, ...

5. −49, −35, −21, −7, ...

6. $\frac{3}{4}, \frac{1}{2}, \frac{1}{4}, 0, ...$

Find the nth term of each arithmetic sequence described.

7. $a_1 = 7, d = 9, n = 18$

8. $a_1 = -12, d = 4, n = 36$

9. −18, −13, −8, −3, ... for $n = 27$

10. 4.1, 4.8, 5.5, 6.2, ... for $n = 14$

11. $a_1 = \frac{3}{8}, d = \frac{1}{4}, n = 15$

12. $a_1 = 2\frac{1}{2}, d = 1\frac{1}{2}, n = 24$

Write an equation for the nth term of each arithmetic sequence. Then graph the first five terms of the sequence.

13. 9, 13, 17, 21, ...

14. −5, −2, 1, 4, ...

15. 19, 31, 43, 55, ...

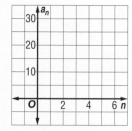

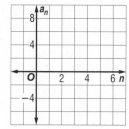

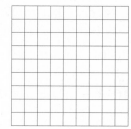

BANKING For Exercises 16 and 17, use the following information.

Chem deposited $115.00 in a savings account. Each week thereafter, he deposits $35.00 into the account.

16. Write a formula to find the total amount Chem has deposited for any particular number of weeks after his initial deposit.

17. How much has Chem deposited 30 weeks after his initial deposit?

18. STORE DISPLAY Tamika is stacking boxes of tissue for a store display. Each row of tissues has 2 fewer boxes than the row below. The first row has 23 boxes of tissues. How many boxes will there be in the tenth row?

4-7 Reading to Learn Mathematics

Arithmetic Sequences

Pre-Activity **How are arithmetic sequences used to solve problems in science?**

Read the introduction to Lesson 4-7 at the top of page 233 in your textbook.
Describe the pattern in the data.

Reading the Lesson

1. Do the recorded altitudes in the introduction form an arithmetic sequence? Explain.

2. What is meant by *successive terms*?

3. Complete the table.

	Pattern	Is the sequence increasing or decreasing?	Is there a common difference? If so, what is it?
a.	2, 5, 8, 11, 14, …		
b.	55, 50, 45, 40, …		
c.	1, 2, 4, 9, 16, …		
d.	$\frac{1}{2}$, 0, $-\frac{1}{2}$, −1, …		
e.	2.6, 2.9, 3.2, 3.5, …		

Helping You Remember

4. Use the pattern 3, 7, 11, 15, … to explain how you would help someone else learn how to find the 10th term of an arithmetic sequence.

4-7 Enrichment

Arithmetic Series

An arithmetic series is a series in which each term after the first may be found by adding the same number to the preceding term. Let S stand for the following series in which each term is 3 more than the preceding one.

$$S = 2 + 5 + 8 + 11 + 14 + 17 + 20$$

The series remains the same if we reverse the order of all the terms. So let us reverse the order of the terms and add one series to the other, term by term. This is shown at the right.

$$
\begin{aligned}
S &= 2 + 5 + 8 + 11 + 14 + 17 + 20 \\
S &= 20 + 17 + 14 + 11 + 8 + 5 + 2 \\
\hline
2S &= 22 + 22 + 22 + 22 + 22 + 22 + 22 \\
2S &= 7(22) \\
S &= \frac{7(22)}{2} = 7(11) = 77
\end{aligned}
$$

Let a represent the first term of the series.

Let ℓ represent the last term of the series.

Let n represent the number of terms in the series.

In the preceding example, $a = 2$, $l = 20$, and $n = 7$. Notice that when you add the two series, term by term, the sum of each pair of terms is 22. That sum can be found by adding the first and last terms, $2 + 20$ or $a + \ell$. Notice also that there are 7, or n, such sums. Therefore, the value of $2S$ is $7(22)$, or $n(a + \ell)$ in the general case. Since this is twice the sum of the series, you can use the following formula to find the sum of any arithmetic series.

$$S = \frac{n(a + \ell)}{2}$$

Example 1 **Find the sum: $1 + 2 + 3 + 4 + 5 + 6 + 7 + 8 + 9$**

$a = 1$, $\ell = 9$, $n = 9$, so $S = \dfrac{9(1 + 9)}{2} = \dfrac{9 \cdot 10}{2} = 45$

Example 2 **Find the sum: $-9 + (-5) + (-1) + 3 + 7 + 11 + 15$**

$a = 29$, $\ell = 15$, $n = 7$, so $S = \dfrac{7(-9 + 15)}{2} = \dfrac{7 \cdot 6}{2} = 21$

Find the sum of each arithmetic series.

1. $3 + 6 + 9 + 12 + 15 + 18 + 21 + 24$

2. $10 + 15 + 20 + 25 + 30 + 35 + 40 + 45 + 50$

3. $-21 + (-16) + (-11) + (-6) + (-1) + 4 + 9 + 14$

4. even whole numbers from 2 through 100

5. odd whole numbers between 0 and 100

4-8 Study Guide and Intervention

Writing Equations from Patterns

Look for Patterns A very common problem-solving strategy is to **look for a pattern**. Arithmetic sequences follow a pattern, and other sequences can follow a pattern.

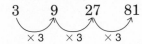 **Example 1** Find the next three terms in the sequence 3, 9, 27, 81, ...

Study the pattern in the sequence.

3   9   27   81
  ×3   ×3   ×3

Successive terms are found by multiplying the last given term by 3.

81   243   729   2187
   ×3   ×3   ×3

The next three terms are 243, 729, 2187.

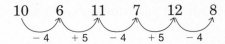 **Example 2** Find the next three terms in the sequence 10, 6, 11, 7, 12, 8, ...

Study the pattern in the sequence.

10   6   11   7   12   8
   −4   +5   −4   +5   −4

Assume that the pattern continues.

8   13   9   14
  +5   −4   +5

The next three terms are 13, 9, 14.

Exercises

1. Give the next two items for the pattern below.

Give the next three numbers in each sequence.

2. 2, 12, 72, 432, ...

3. 7, −14, 28, −56, ...

4. 0, 10, 5, 15, 10, ...

5. 0, 1, 3, 6, 10, ...

6. $x - 1, x - 2, x - 3, ...$

7. $x, \dfrac{x}{2}, \dfrac{x}{3}, \dfrac{x}{4}, ...$

4-8 Study Guide and Intervention *(continued)*

Writing Equations from Patterns

Write Equations Sometimes a pattern can lead to a general rule that can be written as an equation.

Example Suppose you purchased a number of packages of blank compact disks. If each package contains 3 compact disks, you could make a chart to show the relationship between the number of packages of compact disks and the number of disks purchased. Use x for the number of packages and y for the number of compact disks.

Make a table of ordered pairs for several points of the graph.

Number of Packages	1	2	3	4	5
Number of CDs	3	6	9	12	15

The difference in the x values is 1, and the difference in the y values is 3. This pattern shows that y is always three times x. This suggests the relation $y = 3x$. Since the relation is also a function, we can write the equation in functional notation as $f(x) = 3x$.

Exercises

1. Write an equation for the function in functional notation. Then complete the table.

x	−1	0	1	2	3	4
y	−2	2	6			

2. Write an equation for the function in functional notation. Then complete the table.

x	−2	−1	0	1	2	3
y	10	7	4			

3. Write an equation in functional notation.

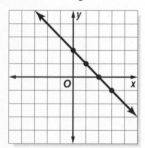

4. Write an equation in functional notation.

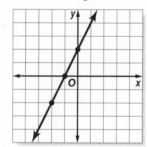

4-8 Skills Practice

Writing Equations from Patterns

Find the next two items for each pattern. Then find the 19th figure in the pattern.

1.

2.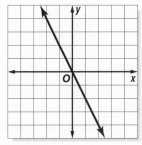

Find the next three terms in each sequence.

3. 1, 4, 10, 19, 31, …   4. 15, 14, 16, 15, 17, 16, …

5. 29, 28, 26, 23, 19, …   6. 2, 3, 2, 4, 2, 5, …

7. x, $x - 1$, $x - 2$, …   8. y, $4y$, $9y$, $16y$, …

Write an equation in function notation for each relation.

9. 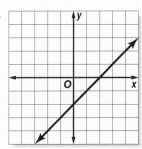   10. 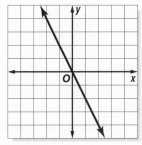   11.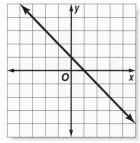

12. 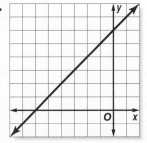   13. 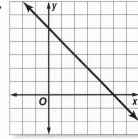   14.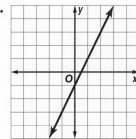

Lesson 4-8

4-8 **Practice**

Writing Equations from Patterns

1. Give the next two items for the pattern. Then find the 21st figure in the pattern.

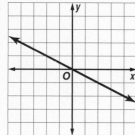

Find the next three terms in each sequence

2. $-5, -2, -3, 0, -1, 2, 1, 4, \ldots$ **3.** $0, 1, 3, 6, 10, 15, \ldots$

4. $0, 1, 8, 27, \ldots$ **5.** $3, 2, 4, 3, 5, 4, \ldots$

6. $a + 1, a + 4, a + 9, \ldots$ **7.** $3d - 1, 4d - 2, 5d - 3, \ldots$

Write an equation in function notation for each relation.

8.
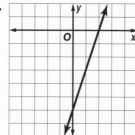

9.

10.
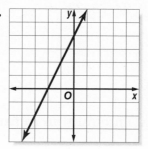

BIOLOGY For Exercises 11 and 12, use the following information.

Male fireflies flash in various patterns to signal location and perhaps to ward off predators. Different species of fireflies have different flash characteristics, such as the intensity of the flash, its rate, and its shape. The table below shows the rate at which a male firefly is flashing.

Time (seconds)	1	2	3	4	5
Number of Flashes	2	4	6	8	10

11. Write an equation in function notation for the relation.

12. How many times will the firefly flash in 20 seconds?

13. GEOMETRY The table shows the number of diagonals that can be drawn from one vertex in a polygon. Write an equation in function notation for the relation and find the number of diagonals that can be drawn from one vertex in a 12-sided polygon.

Sides	3	4	5	6
Diagonals	0	1	2	3

4-8 **Reading to Learn Mathematics**

Writing Equations From Patterns

Pre-Activity **Why is writing equations from patterns important in science?**

Read the introduction to Lesson 4-8 at the top of page 240 in your textbook.

• What is meant by the term *linear pattern*?

• Describe any arithmetic sequences in the data.

Reading the Lesson

1. What is meant by the term *inductive reasoning*?

2. For the figures below, explain why Figure 5 does not follow the pattern.

    1   2   3   4   5

3. Describe the steps you would use to find the pattern in the sequence 1, 5, 25, 125, ...

Helping You Remember

4. What are some basic things to remember when you are trying to discover whether there is a pattern in a sequence of numbers?

© Glencoe/McGraw-Hill

Glencoe Algebra 1

Lesson 4-8

4-8 Enrichment

Traceable Figures

Try to trace over each of the figures below without tracing the same segment twice.

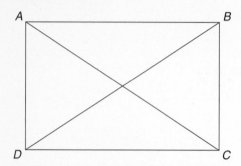

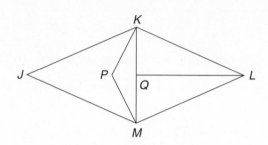

The figure at the left cannot be traced, but the one at the right can. The rule is that a figure is traceable if it has no points, or exactly two points where an odd number of segments meet. The figure at the left has three segments meeting at each of the four corners. However, the figure at the right has exactly two points, L and Q, where an odd number of segments meet.

Determine whether each figure can be traced. If it can, then name the starting point and number the sides in the order in which they should be traced.

1.

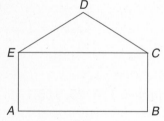

2.

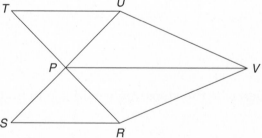

3.

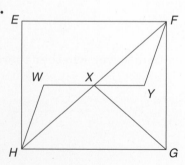

4.

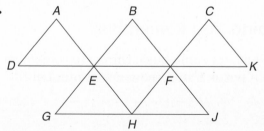

4 **Chapter 4 Test, Form 1** SCORE _____

Write the letter for the correct answer in the blank at the right of each question.

For Questions 1 and 2, use the graph to answer each question.

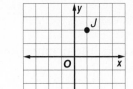

1. Write the ordered pair for point J.
   A. $(1, -2)$ B. $(2, 1)$
   C. $(1, 2)$ D. $(2, -1)$ 1. _____

2. Name the quadrant in which point J is located.
   A. I   B. II   C. III   D. IV   2. _____

3. To plot the point $(1, -2)$, start at the origin and move
   A. left 1 unit and down 2 units.   B. left 2 units and down 1 unit.
   C. left 2 units and up 1 unit.   D. right 1 unit and down 2 units.   3. _____

4. Which best describes a dilation?
   A. a flip   B. an enlargement or reduction
   C. a slide   D. a turn around a point   4. _____

5. Determine what type or transformation is shown.
   A. translation   B. rotation
   C. reflection   D. dilation   5. _____

6. A line segment with end points at point $M(-2, 0)$ and $N(-1, 2)$ is translated 4 units left. What are the coordinates of the endpoints after the transformation is performed?
   A. $M'(-6, -4), N'(-5, -2)$ B. $M'(-6, 0), N'(-5, 2)$
   C. $M'(-2, -4), N'(-1, -2)$ D. $M'(2, 0), N'(3, 2)$ 6. _____

7. Which table, mapping, or graph does *not* show the relation $\{(-1, 1), (1, 2), (2, -2), (4, 3)\}$?

   A.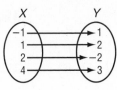

   B.
x	−1	1	2	4
y	1	2	−2	3

   C. 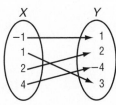   D. 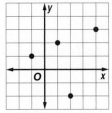   7. _____

8. What is the inverse of the relation $\{(0, 1), (1, 0), (3, -4)\}$?
   A. $\{(0, 0), (1, 1), (3, -4)\}$ B. $\{(0, 1), (1, 0), (3, -4)\}$
   C. $\{(1, 0), (0, 1), (4, -3)\}$ D. $\{(1, 0), (0, 1), (-4, 3)\}$ 8. _____

9. Solve the equation $y = 3x$ if the domain is $\{-1, 0, 1\}$.
   A. $\{(-3, -1), (0, 0), (3, 1)\}$ B. $\{(-1, -3), (0, 0), (1, 3)\}$
   C. $\{(-1, 2), (0, 3), (1, 4)\}$ D. $\{(-1, -1), (0, 0), (1, 1)\}$ 9. _____

10. The distance d a car travels in t hours is given by the function $d = 55t$. Find d when $t = 5$.

   A. 275   **B.** 11   **C.** 60   **D.** 50   10. _____

11. Which equation is a linear equation?

   A. $4m^2 = 6$ **B.** $3a + 5b = -3$ **C.** $\frac{2}{3}xy - \frac{3}{4}y = 0$ **D.** $x^2 + y^2 = 0$ 11. _____

12. Which line shown at the right is the graph of $y = 2x + 4$?

   A. l **B.** the x-axis

   C. p **D.** q 12. _____

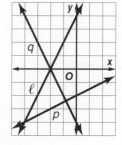

13. Determine which relation is a function.

   A. 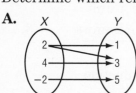   **B.**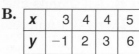

   C. $y = \frac{1}{5}x + 2$ **D.** $\{(3, 0), (-2, -2), (7, -2), (-2, 0)\}$ 13. _____

14. Determine which relation is a function.

   A. $\{(1, 1), (1, 2)\}$ **B.** $x - 5 = 1$ **C.** $y = 9$ **D.** $x = 2$ 14. _____

15. If $h(r) = \frac{2}{3}r - 6$, what is the value of $h(-9)$?

   A. 12   **B.** 0   **C.** -12 **D.** $-6\frac{2}{3}$ 15. _____

16. Determine which sequence is an arithmetic sequence.

   A. 3, 6, 12, 24, ...   **B.** $\frac{1}{5}, \frac{1}{7}, \frac{1}{9}, \frac{1}{11}, ...$

   C. $-7, -3, 1, 5, ...$ **D.** $-10, 5, -\frac{5}{2}, \frac{5}{4}, ...$ 16. _____

17. Find the next three terms of the arithmetic sequence 5, 9, 13, 17, ...

   A. 21   **B.** 21, 25, 29   **C.** 41, 45, 49   **D.** 21, 41, 61   17. _____

18. Find the next two numbers of the sequence 1, 2, 4, 8, 16, ...

   A. 32, 64   **B.** 24, 32   **C.** 20, 22   **D.** 18, 20   18. _____

19. Find the next item in the pattern, ⬜⬜🔲⬜ ⬜⬜⬜🔲 🔲⬜⬜⬜ ⬜🔲⬜⬜ .

   A. 🔲⬜⬜⬜   **B.** ⬜🔲⬜⬜   **C.** ⬜⬜🔲⬜   **D.** ⬜⬜⬜🔲   19. _____

20. Write an equation in function notation for the relation at the right.

   A. $f(x) = 2x$ **B.** $f(x) = -x$

   C. $f(x) = x + 1$ **D.** $f(x) = 1 - x$ 20. _____

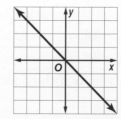

Bonus Solve $y = x - 3$ if the domain is $\{0, 1, 2, 3\}$. Graph the equation $y = x - 3$.   B: _____

4 **Chapter 4 Test, Form 2A** SCORE _____

Write the letter for the correct answer in the blank at the right of each question.

For Questions 1 and 2, use the graph to answer each question.

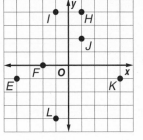

1. Write the ordered pair for point *I*.
   A. $(1, -4)$ **B.** $(-1, 4)$
   C. $(-4, 1)$ **D.** $(4, -1)$ 1. _____

2. Name the quadrant in which point *K* is located.
   A. I **B.** II **C.** III **D.** IV 2. _____

3. To plot the point $(-7, 4)$, start at the origin and move
   A. left 7 units and down 4 units. **B.** left 4 units and down 7 units.
   C. left 7 units and up 4 units. **D.** left 4 units and up 7 units. 3. _____

4. What type of transformation is shown at the right?
   A. reflection **B.** translation
   C. dilation **D.** rotation 4. _____

5. The letter P is flipped over a line. Which transformation is this?
   A. reflection **B.** translation **C.** dilation **D.** rotation 5. _____

6. Triangle *ABC* with $A(-4, -1)$, $B(-2, -1)$, and $C(-4, 4)$ is rotated 180° about the origin. What are the coordinates of the vertices of the figure after the triangle is rotated?
   A. $A'(-1, 4), B'(-1, 2), C'(4, 4)$ **B.** $A'(-1, -4), B'(-1, -2), C'(4, -4)$
   C. $A'(4, 1), B'(2, 1), C'(4, -4)$ **D.** $A'(4, -1), B'(2, -1), C'(4, 4)$ 6. _____

7. State the range of the relation $\{(-2, 5), (0, -1), (-1, 4), (-1, 5)\}$.
   A. $\{-2, 0, -1\}$ **B.** $\{-1, 4, 5\}$ **C.** $\{-2, 0\}$ **D.** $\{-1, 4\}$ 7. _____

8. What is the inverse of the relation $\{(3, -1), (2, 5), (-3, 4), (-2, 0)\}$?
   A. $\{(-3, 1), (-2, -5), (3, -4), (2, 0)\}$ **B.** $\{(-2, 0), (-3, 4), (2, 5), (3, -1)\}$
   C. $\{(-1, 3), (5, 2), (4, -3), (0, -2)\}$ **D.** $\{(1, -3), (-5, -2), (-4, 3), (0, 2)\}$ 8. _____

9. Solve $y = 2x - 7$ if the domain is $\{-3, 1, 5\}$.
   A. $\{(-3, -1), (1, -9), (5, -17)\}$ **B.** $\{(-3, -10), (1, -6), (5, -2)\}$
   C. $\{(-3, -13), (1, -5), (5, 3)\}$ **D.** $\{(-3, -6), (1, 2), (5, 10)\}$ 9. _____

10. Which equation is *not* a linear equation?
    A. $-4v + 2w = 7$ **B.** $\frac{x}{4} = y$ **C.** $x = -5$ **D.** $\frac{2}{x} + \frac{3}{y} = 6$ 10. _____

11. If $g(x) = 3x^2 - 4x + 1$, what is the value of $g(-2)$?
    A. 21 **B.** 29 **C.** 45 **D.** 5 11. _____

12. Find the next two numbers of the sequence 7, 11, 8, 12, 9, 13, 10, ...
    A. 11, 15 **B.** 14, 15 **C.** 14, 11 **D.** 15, 12 12. _____

Chapter 4 Test, Form 2A *(continued)*

13. Which is the graph of $2x - y = 1$ if the domain is $\{-2, -1, 0, 1, 2\}$? **13.** ______

A.

B.

C.

D.

14. Which line shown at the right is the graph of $x - 2y = 4$?

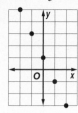

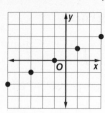

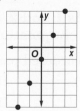

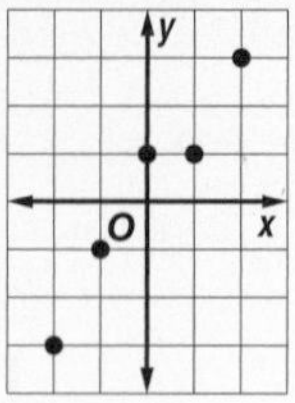

A. l **B.** m

C. p **D.** q

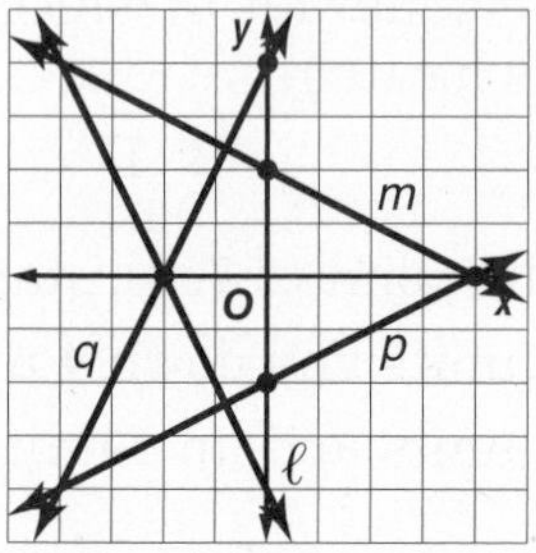

14. ______

15. Which equation has a graph that is a vertical line?

A. $2x = y$ **B.** $3x - 2 = 0$

C. $y + 5 = 3$ **D.** $x - y = 0$ **15.** ______

16. Determine which relation is *not* a function.

A.

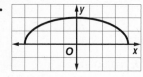

B.

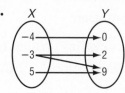

C.

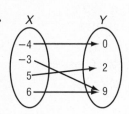

D.

x	−2	0	1	3
y	0	0	2	1

16. ______

17. Determine which sequence is *not* an arithmetic sequence.

A. $-7, 0, 7, 14, \ldots$ **B.** $0, \frac{1}{2}, 1, \frac{3}{2}, \ldots$ **C.** $10, 6, 2, -2, \ldots$ **D.** $2, 4, 8, 16, \ldots$ **17.** ______

18. Which equation describes the nth term of the arithmetic sequence 7, 10, 13, 16, …?

A. $a_n = 3n + 4$ **B.** $a_n = 7 + 3n$ **C.** $a_n = -4n + 3$ **D.** $a_n = 3n - 4$ **18.** ______

19. Find the next two items in the pattern .

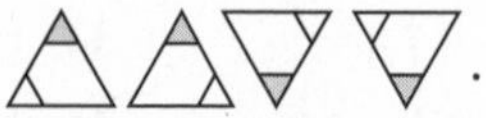

A.   **B.**   **C.**   **D.**   **19.** ______

20. Write an equation in function notation for the relation shown at the right.

A. $f(x) = -2x$ **B.** $f(x) = x - 2$

C. $f(x) = 2x + 2$ **D.** $f(x) = -x + 2$

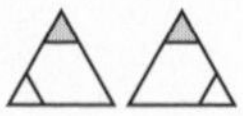

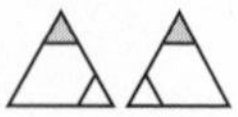

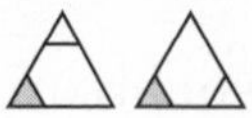

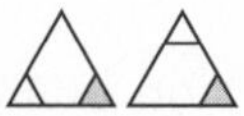

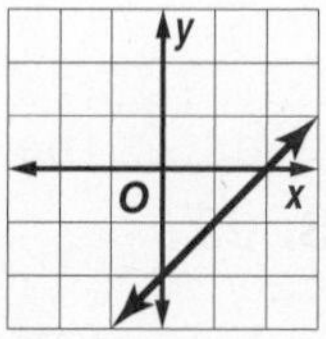

20. ______

Bonus Find the solution set of $2x - y^2 = 8$, given the replacement set $\{(2, -2), (6, 2), (6, 22), (4, 0), (12, -4)\}$. **B:** ______________

4 Chapter 4 Test, Form 2B

SCORE _____

Write the letter for the correct answer in the blank at the right of each question.

For Questions 1 and 2, use the graph to answer each question.

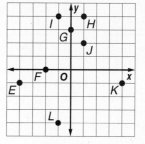

1. Write the ordered pair for point *L*.
   A. (1, −4)   **B.** (−4, 1)
   C. (−1, −4)   **D.** (−4, −1)

1. _____

2. Name the quadrant in which point *E* is located.
   A. I   **B.** II   **C.** III   **D.** IV

2. _____

3. To plot the point (−5, 2), start at the origin and move
   A. right 2 units and down 5 units.   **B.** left 5 units and up 2 units.
   C. left 5 units and down 2 units.   **D.** right 2 units and up 5 units.

3. _____

4. What type of transformation is shown at the right?
   A. reflection   **B.** translation
   C. dilation   **D.** rotation

4. _____

5. A letter R is turned around a point. Which type of transformation is this?
   A. reflection   **B.** translation   **C.** dilation   **D.** rotation

5. _____

6. Triangle *HIJ* with *H*(−2, 1), *I*(1, 4), and *J*(3, 1) is reflected over the *x*-axis. What are the coordinates of the vertices of the figure after the triangle is reflected?
   A. $H'(-2, -1), I'(1, -4), J'(3, -1)$ **B.** $H'(2, 1), I'(-1, 4), J'(-3, 1)$
   C. $H'(2, -1), I'(-1, -4), J'(-3, -1)$ **D.** $H'(1, -2), I'(4, 1), J'(1, 3)$

6. _____

7. What is the range of the relation {(5, 3), (2, 8), (−1, 1), (6, 1)}?
   A. {(−1, 1), (6, 1)}   **B.** {−1, 2, 5, 6}
   C. {1, 3, 8}   **D.** {3, 8}

7. _____

8. What is the inverse of the relation {(−2, −1), (2, 1), (−2, 4), (−4, 0)}?
   A. {(−4, 0), (−2, 4), (2, 1), (−2, −1)}   **B.** {(2, 1), (−2, −1), (2, −4), (4, 0)}
   C. {(1, 2), (−1, −2), (−4, 2), (0, 4)}   **D.** {(−1, −2), (1, 2), (4, −2), (0, −4)}

8. _____

9. Solve $y = -2x + 8$ if the domain is {−2, 0, 4}.
   A. {(−2, 12), (0, 8), (4, 0)}   **B.** {(−2, 4), (0, 8), (4, 0)}
   C. {(−2, 6), (0, 8), (4, 12)}   **D.** {(−2, 4), (0, 0), (4, −8)}

9. _____

10. Which equation is *not* a linear equation?
    A. $2x + 5y = 3$ **B.** $y = -10$ **C.** $5 = 3xy$ **D.** $y = \frac{x}{7} + 4$

10. _____

11. If $f(x) = 2x^2 - 3x + 5$, what is the value of $f(-3)$?
    A. 14   **B.** 50   **C.** 2   **D.** 32

11. _____

12. Find the next two numbers of the sequence 1, 8, 5, 12, 9, 16, 13, ...
    A. 24, 21   **B.** 20, 17   **C.** 20, 24   **D.** 17, 21

12. _____

13. Which is the graph of $2x + y = -5$ if the domain is $\{-4, -3, -2, -1, 0\}$?

A.  **B.** 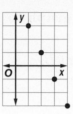 **C.** 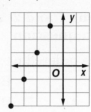 **D.** 13. _____

14. Which line shown at the right is the graph of $x + 2y = 6$?

A. r **B.** s

C. t **D.** v 14. _____

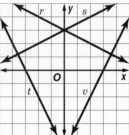

15. Which equation has a graph that is a horizontal line?

A. $x - 7 = 0$ **B.** $x = y$

C. $2y + 3 = 4$ **D.** $x + y = 0$ 15. _____

16. Determine which relation is a function.

A.  **B.** 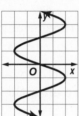 **C.** 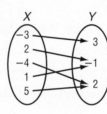 **D.**

x	y
-2	7
0	0
1	-2
1	3

16. _____

17. Determine which sequence is an arithmetic sequence.

A. $-16, -12, -8, -4, \ldots$ **B.** $1, 4, 2, 5, 3, \ldots$

C. $4, 8, 16, 32, \ldots$ **D.** $1, 1, 2, 3, 5, \ldots$ 17. _____

18. Which equation describes the nth term of the arithmetic sequence $-12, -14, -16, -18, \ldots$?

A. $a_n = -2n - 10$ **B.** $a_n = -12 - 2n$

C. $a_n = 10n - 2$ **D.** $a_n = -2n + 10$ 18. _____

19. Find the next two items in the pattern, .

A.   **B.** **C.** **D.** 19. _____

20. Write an equation in function notation for the relation.

A. $f(x) = -2x$ **B.** $f(x) = -x + 2$

C. $f(x) = x - 2$ **D.** $f(x) = 2x + 2$ 20. _____

Bonus If $f(x) = x - x^2$, find $f(2m + 3)$. **B:** _____

4 Chapter 4 Test, Form 2C

SCORE _____

Write the ordered pair for each point shown at the right. Name the quadrant in which the point is located.

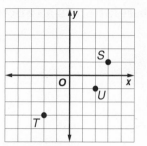

1. S 2. T

3. U

1. _____

2. _____

3. _____

Plot each point on a coordinate plane.

4. $A(3, 2)$ 5. $B(0, -2)$ 6. $C(-3, 4)$

4–6.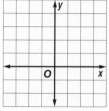

For Questions 7 and 8, determine whether each transformation is a *reflection, translation, dilation,* or *rotation.*

7.

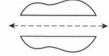

8.

7. _____

8. _____

9.

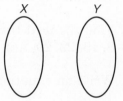

9. Express the relation $\{(1, 4), (-2, 3), (-5, 0), (7, 4), (3, 2)\}$ as a mapping. Then determine the domain and range.

10. Express the relation shown in the graph as a set of ordered pairs. Then write the inverse of the relation.

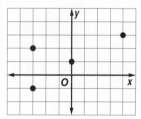

10. _____

11. Find the solution set for $x - 2y = 9$, given the replacement set $\{(-1, -5), (3, -3), (5, 2), (7, 1)\}$.

11. _____

12. _____

12. Solve $y = -2x + 1$ if the domain is $\{-2, -1, 0, 1, 2\}$. Graph the solution set.

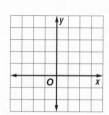

For Questions 13 and 14, determine whether each equation is a linear equation. If so, write the equation in standard form.

13. $xy = 6$ 14. $2x + 3y + 7 = 3$

13. _____

14. _____

15. Graph the equation $x - 4y = 2$.

15.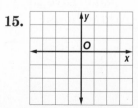

4 **Chapter 4 Test, Form 2C** *(continued)*

Determine whether each relation is a function.

16.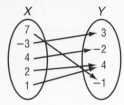

17.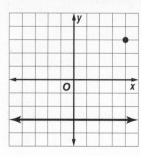

16. _____

17. _____

18. _____

For Questions 18 and 19, if $f(x) = x^2 + 3x - 2$, find each value.

18. $f(2)$ 19. $f(5v)$

19. _____

20. _____

20. Determine whether the sequence $-10, -7, -4, -1, \ldots$ is an arithmetic sequence. If so, state the common difference.

21. _____

21. Find the next three terms of the arithmetic sequence $8, 15, 22, 29, \ldots \}$.

22. _____

22. Write an equation for the nth term of the sequence $12, 5, -2, -9, \ldots$. Then graph the first five terms of the sequence.

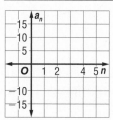

23. Find the next two items in the pattern, 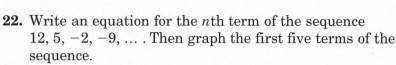.

23. _____

24. Use the table below that shows the amount of gasoline a car consumes for different distances driven.

24. _____

distance (mi)	1	2	3	4	5
gasoline (gal)	0.04	0.08	0.12	0.16	0.20

Write an equation in function notation for the relationship between distance and gasoline used.

25. Maya wants to enlarge a rectangular cartoon that is 2 inches wide and 3 inches tall by a scale factor of 1.5. What will be the dimensions of the new cartoon? Use a coordinate system to draw a picture of the original cartoon and the enlarged cartoon. Place one corner of each cartoon at the origin and for each cartoon write the coordinates of the other three vertices.

25. _____

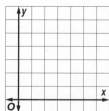

Bonus Graph $x = 3$, $y = -1$, and $2x - 2y = 0$ on a coordinate plane. Give the vertices of the figure formed by the three lines.

B:

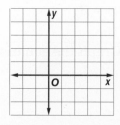

          Glencoe Algebra 1

4 ## Chapter 4 Test, Form 2D

SCORE _____

Write the ordered pair for each point shown at the right. Name the quadrant in which the point is located.

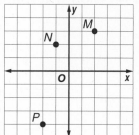

1. *M*

2. *N*

3. *P*

1. _____

2. _____

3. _____

Plot each point on a coordinate plane.

4. *A*(−3, 0)   5. *B*(2, −2)   6. *C*(1, 3)

4-6.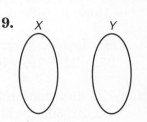

For Questions 7 and 8, determine whether each transformation is a *reflection*, *translation*, *dilation*, or *rotation*.

7.

8.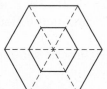

7. _____

8. _____

9.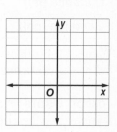

9. Express the relation {(8, 7), (−2, 0), (1, 0), (4, −5), (−1, 3)} as a mapping. Then determine the domain and range.

10. Express the relation shown in the graph as a set of ordered pairs. Then write the inverse of the relation.

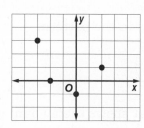

11. Find the solution set for $3x - y = 7$, given the replacement set {(2, 1), (−3, −16), (5, 8), (4, −19)}.

10. _____

11. _____

12. _____

12. Solve $y = -2x - 1$ if the domain is {−3, −2, −1, 0, 1}. Graph the solution set.

For Questions 13 and 14, determine whether each equation is a linear equation. If so, write the equation in standard form.

13. $\frac{1}{x} + \frac{1}{y} = \frac{2}{3}$

14. $4x = 2y$

15. Graph the equation $x + 4y - 3 = 0$.

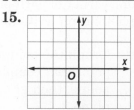

13. _____

14. _____

15.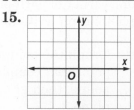

Determine whether each relation is a function.

16.

x	y
-2	7
0	0
1	-2
1	3

17.

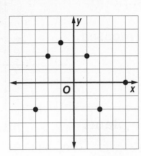

For Questions 18 and 19, if $g(x) = x^2 - 2x + 4$, find each value.

18. $g(-5)$ 19. $g(t - 1)$

20. Determine whether the sequence 7, 11, 15, 19, … is an arithmetic sequence. If so, state the common difference.

21. Find the next three terms of the arithmetic sequence -25, -22, -19, -16, … .

22. Write an equation for the *n*th term of the sequence 3, 12, 21, 30, … . Then graph the first five terms of the sequence.

23. Find the next two items in the pattern.

 …

24. Use the table below that shows the amount of gasoline a car consumes for different distances driven.

Distance (mi)	1	2	3	4	5
Gasoline (gal)	0.05	0.10	0.15	0.20	0.25

Write an equation in function notation for the relationship between distance and gasoline used.

25. Joseph wants to reduce a rectangular photograph that is 3 inches wide and 5 inches tall by a scale factor of 2.5 so it will fit on his report. What will be the dimensions of the new photograph? Use a coordinate system to draw a photograph of the original rectangle and the reduced photograph. Place one corner of each photograph at the origin and for each photograph write the coordinates of the other three vertices.

Bonus Graph the points (4, -2), (4, 3), (-2, 3). Find a fourth point that completes a rectangle with the given three points, then graph the rectangle on the same coordinate plane.

16. _____

17. _____

18. _____

19. _____

20. _____

21. _____

22. _____

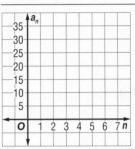

23. _____

24. _____

25. _____

B: _____

4 **Chapter 4 Test, Form 3**   SCORE _____

1. Write the ordered pair that describes a point 8 units below the origin and on the y-axis.

1. _____

2. Plot the points $(-3, 1.5)$ and $\left(\frac{3}{2}, -4\right)$ on a coordinate plane, and label each point with the ordered pairs.

2.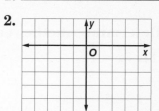

3. Determine whether a *reflection*, *translation*, *dilation*, or *rotation* is being shown.

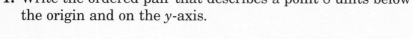

3. _____

4. _____

4. Triangle MNP with $M(1, 2)$, $N(3, 4)$, and $P(4, -1)$ is reflected over the y-axis, then translated 2 units right and 2 units down. Find the coordinates of the vertices after the given transformations are performed. Then, graph the preimage and its image.

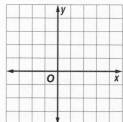

5. Express the relation $\{(4, -1), (-2, 3), (-1, -2), (6, -2), (3, -1)\}$ as a mapping. Then determine the domain and range.

5.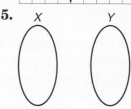

6. Express the relation shown in the graph as a set of ordered pairs. Then write the inverse of the relation.

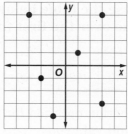

6. _____

7. Find the solution set for $4x - 5y = 15$, given the replacement set $\{(-10, -12), (-3, -5.4), (5, 1.2), (6, 3), (15, 9)\}$.

7. _____

8. _____

8. Solve the equation $7x + 2y = 8$ if the domain is $\{-4, 3, 5, 6\}$. Graph the solution set.

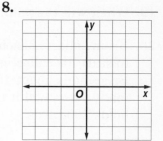

9. Determine whether $3x - 4y + 7 = 3y + 1$ is a linear equation. If so, write the equation in standard form.

9. _____

Assessment

10. Graph $\frac{2x}{3} = \frac{y}{2} - 1$.

10.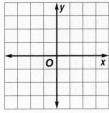

Determine whether each relation is a function.

11. $3x = 11$ **12.**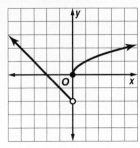

11. _____

12. _____

13. If $f(x) = 3x^2 - 4x$, find $-2[f(2p)]$.

13. _____

14. Determine whether the sequence $0, \frac{1}{2}, 1, \frac{3}{2}, \dots$ is an arithmetic sequence. If it is, state the common difference.

14. _____

15. Find the value of y that makes $9, 4, y, -6, \dots$ an arithmetic sequence.

15. _____

16. Write an equation for the nth term of the arithmetic sequence $-15, -11, -7, -3, \dots$. Then graph the first five terms of the sequence.

16. _____

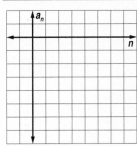

17. Find the tenth figure in the pattern below.

For Questions 18 and 19, use the table below that shows the value of a vending machine over the first five years of use.

Number of years	0	1	2	3	4	5
Value (dollars)	2000	1810	1620	1430	1240	1050

17. _____

18. Write an equation in function notation for the relationship between years of use t and value $v(t)$.

18. _____

19. When will the value of the vending machine reach 0?

19. _____

20. Brian collects baseball cards. His father gave him 20 cards to start his collection on his tenth birthday. Each year Brian adds about 15 cards to his collection. About how many years will it take to fill his collection binder if it holds 200 cards?

20. _____

B: _____

Bonus Solve the equation $\frac{x}{2} - \frac{y}{3} = 10$ if the domain is $\{-4, -1, 2, 3, 6\}$. Then state the inverse of the solution set.

4 Chapter 4 Open-Ended Assessment

Demonstrate your knowledge by giving a clear, concise solution to each problem. Be sure to include all relevant drawings and justify your answers. You may show your solution in more than one way or investigate beyond the requirements of the problem.

1. **a.** Give the coordinates of a point on the coordinate plane. Name the quadrant in which the point is located.

   b. Reflect the point in part **a** across the y-axis and find the coordinates of the image. Graph the preimage and its image.

   c. Explain how the coordinates of a point can be determined to be positive or negative by knowing in which quadrant the point is located.

2. **a.** List any two transformations and describe the differences between the two transformations chosen.

   b. Describe any similarities between the two transformations chosen for part **a**.

3. Use the set $\{-1, 0, 1, 2\}$ as a domain and the set $\{-3, -1, 4, 5\}$ as a range.

   a. Create a relation. Express the relation as a set of ordered pairs. Then state the inverse of the relation.

   b. Create a relation that is *not* a function. Express the relation as a table, a graph, and a mapping.

   c. Explain why the relation created for part **b** is not a function.

4. Write a linear equation in standard form. Then explain how to graph the equation.

5. An equation is written using the function notation $f(x)$. Explain what $f(2)$ represents and describe how to find $f(2)$.

6. **a.** Write a sequence that is an arithmetic sequence. State the common difference, and find a_6.

   b. Write a sequence that is not an arithmetic sequence. Determine whether the sequence has a pattern, and if so describe the pattern.

   c. Determine if the sequence 1, 1, 1, 1, ... is an arithmetic sequence. Explain your reasoning.

Assessment

4 Chapter 4 Vocabulary Test/Review

arithmetic sequence	image	reflection	*x*-axis
axes	inductive reasoning	rotation	*x*-coordinate
common difference	inverse	sequence	*x*-intercept
coordinate plane	linear equation	solution	*y*-axis
dilation	look for a pattern	standard form	*y*-coordinate
equation in two variables	mapping	terms	*y*-intercept
function	origin	transformation	
function notation	preimage	translation	
graph	quadrant	vertical line test	

Choose from the terms above to complete each sentence.

1. In mathematics, points are located in reference to two

perpendicular number lines called _____.

2. The axes in the coordinate plane intersect at a common zero

point called the _____.

3. The *x*-axis and *y*-axis separate the coordinate plane into four

regions called _____.

4. _____ are movements of geometric figures.

5. In a(n) _____, a figure is slid horizontally,
vertically, or both.

6. The _____ of any relation is obtained by
switching the coordinates of each ordered pair of the relation.

7. For a(n) _____ $Ax + By = C$, the numbers
$A, B,$ and C cannot all be zero.

8. A(n) _____ is a relation in which each
element of the domain is paired with exactly one element of the
range.

9. The _____ can be used to determine if a
graph represents a function.

In your own words—
Define each term.

10. coordinate plane

11. mapping

4 Chapter 4 Quiz
(Lessons 4–1 and 4–2)

Write the ordered pair for each point shown. Name the quadrant in which the point is located.

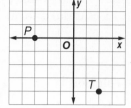

1. *P*
2. *T*

1. _____

2. _____

For Questions 3 and 4, identify each transformation as a *reflection*, *translation*, *dilation*, or *rotation*.

3. _____

3.

4.

4. _____

5. _____

5. Find the coordinates of the vertices of triangle *ABC* with *A*(1, 2), *B*(3, 3), and *C*(3, −1), after the triangle is reflected over the *y*-axis. Then graph the preimage and its image.

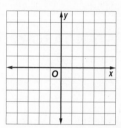

- -

4 Chapter 4 Quiz
(Lessons 4–3 and 4–4)

1. Express the relation {(3, 5), (−4, 6), (3, 8), (2, 4), (1, 3)} as a mapping. Then determine the domain and range.

1.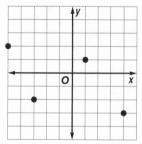

2. Express the relation shown in the graph as a set of ordered pairs. Then write the inverse of the relation.

3. Find the solution set for $y = 4x - 3$, given the replacement set {(−3, 9), (−2, −11), (0, −2), (2, 5)}.

2. _____

4. Solve $3x - 2y = -6$ if the domain is {−2, −1, 0, 2, 3}.

5. Solve the equation $y = 2x + 4$ if the domain is {−3, −2, −1, 0, 1}.

3. _____

4. _____

5. _____

Glencoe Algebra 1

Assessment

4 Chapter 4 Quiz

SCORE _____

(Lessons 4–5 and 4–6)

1. Determine whether $y = 2x - 1$ is a linear equation. If so, write the equation in standard form.

1. _____

2. Graph $3x - y = 3$.

2.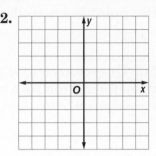

3. Determine whether the relation is a function.

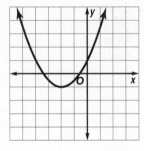

3. _____

4. If $g(x) = x^2 - 3x + 2$, find $g(-4)$.

4. _____

5. **STANDARDIZED TEST PRACTICE** If $\ll x \gg = x^2 - 3x + 4$, then $\ll 6 \gg =$

   A. -8.   **B.** 22.   **C.** 58.   **D.** 14.

5. _____

---

4 Chapter 4 Quiz

SCORE _____

(Lessons 4–7 and 4–8)

1. Determine whether 2, 5, 9, 14, … is an arithmetic sequence. If so, state the common difference.

1. _____

2. Find the next three terms of the arithmetic sequence 5, 9, 13, 17, … .

2. _____

3. Find the 15th term of the arithmetic sequence if $a_1 = -3$ and $d = 2$.

3. _____

4. Find the next three terms in the sequence 3125, 625, 125, 25, … .

4. _____

5. Write an equation in function notation for the relation graphed.

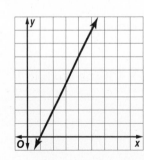

5. _____

4 # Chapter 4 Mid-Chapter Test

SCORE _____

(Lessons 4–1 through 4–4)

Part I *Write the letter for the correct answer in the blank at the right of each question.*

1. Write the ordered pair for
   point P and name the quadrant
   in which it is located.
   A. $(2, -3)$; II   **B.** $(2, -3)$; III
   C. $(-2, -3)$; III   **D.** $(-2, -3)$; II

   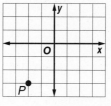

   1. _____

2. Determine what type of
   transformation is shown.
   A. reflection   **B.** translation
   C. dilation   **D.** rotation

   2. _____

3. What is the inverse of the relation $\{(-1, 2), (3, -4), (0, 5)\}$?
   A. $\{(2, -1), (-4, 3), (5, 0)\}$ **B.** $\{(-2, 1), (4, -3), (-5, 0)\}$
   C. $\{(1, -2), (-3, 4), (0, -5)\}$ **D.** $\{(1, 2), (-3, -4), (0, 5)\}$

   3. _____

For Questions 4 and 5 use the following information.
The total T charged by a phone company can be represented
by the equation $T = 30 + 0.10m$ where m is the number of minutes.

4. Solve the equation for m.

   A. $m = \dfrac{T}{0.10} - 30$ **B.** $m = 0.1(T - 30)$ **C.** $m = \dfrac{T}{0.10} + 30$ **D.** $m = \dfrac{T - 30}{0.10}$

   4. _____

5. Find the number of minutes if the total charge is $31.00.
   A. 100   **B.** 10   **C.** 1   **D.** 340

   5. _____

Part II

6. Express the relation $\{(-3, -2), (3, -1), (5, -2), (7, 0)\}$
   as a mapping.

   6.

7. For the triangle described below, find the coordinates of the
   vertices of each figure after the given transformation is
   performed. Then graph the preimage and its image.
   Triangle DEF with $D(-1, 1)$, $E(-4, 1)$, and $F(-2, 4)$
   reflected over the y-axis

   7. _____

Solve each equation for the given domain.

8. $y = 2x - 3$ for $x = \{-2, -1, 0, 2, 3\}$

   8. _____

9. $3y - x = 6$ for $x = \{-3, 0, 3, 6\}$

   9. _____

Glencoe Algebra 1

Assessment

4 # Chapter 4 Cumulative Review
(Chapters 1–4)

1. Find the solution of $y + \frac{2}{3} = \frac{22}{15}$ if the replacement set is $\left\{ \frac{2}{5}, \frac{3}{5}, \frac{4}{5}, 1, 1\frac{1}{5} \right\}$. (Lesson 1–3)

2. Simplify $5m + 8n + 3m + n$. (Lesson 1–6)

3. The average longevity in years of 10 different farm animals is listed below. Make a stem-and-leaf plot. (Lesson 2–5)
   12 12 12 15 12 8 20 10 5 12

4. Find $\sqrt{38}$. Round to the nearest hundredth. (Lesson 2–7)

5. Translate the following equation into a verbal sentence.
   $\frac{x}{4} - y = -2\left(\frac{x}{y} \right)$
   (Lesson 3–1)

6. Find the discounted price. clock: $15.00
   discount: 15% (Lesson 3–7)

7. Solve $-7x + 23 = 37$. (Lesson 3–4)

8. Use cross products to determine whether the ratios $\frac{4}{7}$ and $\frac{11}{15}$ form a proportion. Write *yes* or *no*. (Lesson 3–6)

1. _____

2. _____

3.

4. _____

5. _____

6. _____

7. _____

8. _____

9. _____

10. _____

For Questions 9–11, use the graph.

9. Write the ordered pair for point A, and name the quadrant in which the point is located. (Lesson 4–1)

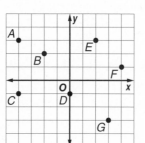

10. Express the relation as a set of ordered pairs. Then determine the domain and range. (Lesson 4–3)

11. Determine whether the relation is a function. (Lesson 4–6)

12. Find the coordinates of the vertices of triangle ABC with $A(-1, 0)$, $B(2, 4)$, and $C(3, 1)$ reflected over the x-axis. Then graph the preimage and its image. (Lesson 4–2)

13. Solve $4x = 5 + y$ if the domain is $\{-3, -1, 1, 2, 5\}$. (Lesson 4–4)

14. Graph $2x - 3y = 6$. (Lesson 4–5)

11. _____

12. _____

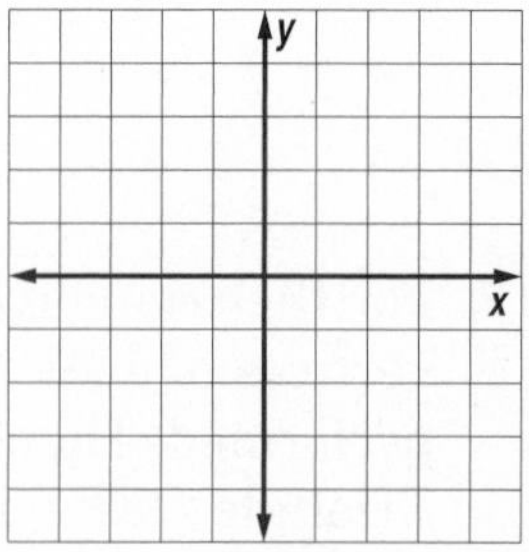

13. _____

14.
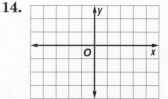

4 Standardized Test Practice
(Chapters 1–4)

Part 1: Multiple Choice

Instructions: Fill in the appropriate oval for the best answer.

1. Which vehicle is a counterexample for the statement.
   If an automobile is a sports car, then it is red. (Lesson 1–7)
   A. a red pick-up truck   **B.** a white motor home
   C. a red sports car   **D.** a yellow sports car   1. Ⓐ Ⓑ Ⓒ Ⓓ

2. Dion owns a delivery service. He charges his customers $15.00
   for each delivery. His expenses include $7000 for the motorcycle
   he drives and $0.42 for gasoline per trip. Which equation could
   Dion use to calculate his profit p for d deliveries? (Lesson 1–8)
   E. $p = 15 - 0.42d$ **F.** $p = 14.58d - 7000$
   G. $p = 7000 + 15d$ **H.** $p = 0.42d + 7000$ 2. Ⓔ Ⓕ Ⓖ Ⓗ

3. Evaluate $-4xy$ if $x = 5.3$ and $y = -0.4$. (Lesson 2–3)
   A. 9.7   **B.** -9.7 **C.** 8.48   **D.** -8.48 3. Ⓐ Ⓑ Ⓒ Ⓓ

4. Which measure of central tendency best represents the data?
   new car prices: $14,500, $12,400, $18,500, $12,400, $28,900,
   $19,100, $17,300, $22,900, $17,800, $21,600 (Lesson 2–5)
   E. median   **F.** mean   **G.** mode   **H.** none   4. Ⓔ Ⓕ Ⓖ Ⓗ

5. Translate the sentence into an equation. (Lesson 3–1)
   Five times the sum of s and t is as much as four times r.
   A. $5s + t = 4$ **B.** $5s + t = r$ **C.** $5(s + t) = 4r$ **D.** $s + t = 5(4r)$ 5. Ⓐ Ⓑ Ⓒ Ⓓ

6. Solve $8(x - 5) = 12(4x - 1) + 12$. (Lesson 3–5)
   E. $-\dfrac{7}{10}$ **F.** $-\dfrac{5}{7}$ **G.** -2 **H.** -1 6. Ⓔ Ⓕ Ⓖ Ⓗ

7. Paul and Charlene are 420 miles apart. They start toward each
   other with Paul driving 16 miles per hour faster than Charlene.
   They meet in 5 hours. Find Charlene's speed. (Lesson 3–9)
   A. 34 mph   **B.** 50 mph   **C.** 40.4 mph   **D.** 68 mph   7. Ⓐ Ⓑ Ⓒ Ⓓ

8. Determine which equation is a linear equation. (Lesson 4–5)
   E. $x^2 + y = 4$ **F.** $x + y = 4$ **G.** $xy = 4$ **H.** $\dfrac{1}{x} + y = 4$ 8. Ⓔ Ⓕ Ⓖ Ⓗ

9. If $f(x) = 7 - 2x$, find $f(3) + 6$. (Lesson 4–6)
   A. 11   **B.** 7   **C.** 14   **D.** –11   9. Ⓐ Ⓑ Ⓒ Ⓓ

10. Chapa is beginning an exercise program that calls for 30 push-ups
    each day for the first week. Each week thereafter, she has to
    increase her push-ups by 2. Which week of her program will be
    the first one in which she will do 50 push-ups a day? (Lesson 4–7)
    E. 9th week   **F.** 10th week   **G.** 11th week   **H.** 12th week   10. Ⓔ Ⓕ Ⓖ Ⓗ

Assessment

4 **Standardized Test Practice** *(continued)*

Instructions: Enter your answer by writing each digit of the answer in a column box and then shading in the appropriate oval that corresponds to that entry.

11. Evaluate $27 + |y + z|$ if $y = -4.9$ and $z = -5.1$. (Lesson 2–1)

12. The ratio of a to b is $\frac{4}{7}$. If a is 16, find the value of b. (Lesson 3–6)

13. Tariq is enlarging a map by a scale factor of $3\frac{1}{2}$. On his original map the distance from his home to his school is 4 inches. How far in inches is this distance on the enlargement? (Lesson 4–2)

14. The equation $C = \dfrac{F - 32}{1.8}$ relates the temperature in degrees Fahrenheit F to degrees Celsius C. If the temperature is $25°C$ in Rome, Italy, what is the temperature in degrees Fahrenheit? (Lesson 4–4)

11. 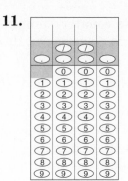 **12.**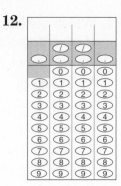

13. 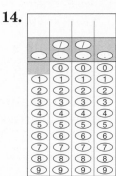 **14.**

Instructions: Compare the quantities in columns A and B. Shade in
- Ⓐ if the quantity in column A is greater;
- Ⓑ if the quantity in column B is greater;
- Ⓒ if the quantities are equal; or
- Ⓓ if the relationship cannot be determined from the information given.

	Column A	**Column B**	
15.	$\dfrac{14 + 7a}{7}$	$3(a - 2)$	**15.** Ⓐ Ⓑ Ⓒ Ⓓ
	(Lessons 2–3 and 2–4)		
16.	Given: $x - 4 = 10$		**16.** Ⓐ Ⓑ Ⓒ Ⓓ
	x	15	
	(Lesson 3–2)		
17.	the quadrant in which point $(-3, -1)$ is located	the quadrant in which point $(-2, 4)$ is located	**17.** Ⓐ Ⓑ Ⓒ Ⓓ
	(Lesson 4–1)		

4 Standardized Test Practice

Student Record Sheet *(Use with pages 252–253 of the Student Edition.)*

Part 1 Multiple Choice

Select the best answer from the choices given and fill in the corresponding oval.

1 Ⓐ Ⓑ Ⓒ Ⓓ   4 Ⓐ Ⓑ Ⓒ Ⓓ   7 Ⓐ Ⓑ Ⓒ Ⓓ

2 Ⓐ Ⓑ Ⓒ Ⓓ   5 Ⓐ Ⓑ Ⓒ Ⓓ   8 Ⓐ Ⓑ Ⓒ Ⓓ

3 Ⓐ Ⓑ Ⓒ Ⓓ   6 Ⓐ Ⓑ Ⓒ Ⓓ   9 Ⓐ Ⓑ Ⓒ Ⓓ

Part 2 Short Response/Grid In

Solve the problem and write your answer in the blank.

Also enter your answer by writing each number or symbol in a box.
Then fill in the corresponding oval for that number or symbol.

10 _____ (grid in)

11 _____

12 _____

13 _____ (grid in)

14 _____ (grid in)

15 _____ (grid in)

16 _____ (grid in)

10   13   14
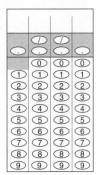

15   16
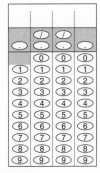
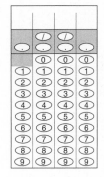

Part 3 Quantitative Comparison

Select the best answer from the choices given and fill in the corresponding oval.

17 Ⓐ Ⓑ Ⓒ Ⓓ   18 Ⓐ Ⓑ Ⓒ Ⓓ   19 Ⓐ Ⓑ Ⓒ Ⓓ   20 Ⓐ Ⓑ Ⓒ Ⓓ

Part 4 Open-Ended

Record your answers for Question 21 on the back of this paper.

Answers

4-1 Study Guide and Intervention

The Coordinate Plane

Identify Points In the diagram at the right, points are located in reference to two perpendicular number lines called **axes**. The horizontal number line is the **x-axis**, and the vertical number line is the **y-axis**. The plane containing the x- and y-axes is called the **coordinate plane**. Points in the coordinate plane are named by ordered pairs of the form (x, y). The first number, or **x-coordinate**, corresponds to a number on the x-axis. The second number, or **y-coordinate**, corresponds to a number on the y-axis.

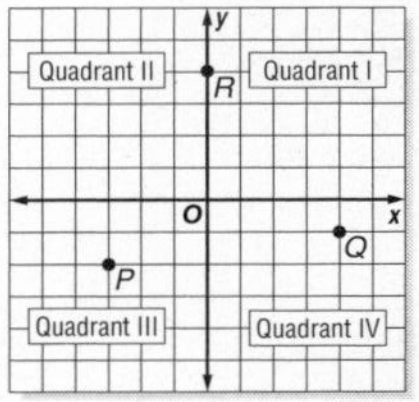

The axes divide the coordinate plane into Quadrants I, II, III, and IV, as shown. The point where the axes intersect is called the **origin**. The origin has coordinates (0, 0).

Example 1 Write an ordered pair for point R above.

The x-coordinate is 0 and the y-coordinate is 4. Thus the ordered pair for R is (0, 4).

Example 2 Write ordered pairs for points P and Q above. Then name the quadrant in which each point is located.

The x-coordinate of P is -3 and the y-coordinate is -2. Thus the ordered pair for P is $(-3, -2)$. P is in Quadrant III.

The x-coordinate of Q is 4 and the y-coordinate is -1. Thus the ordered pair for Q is $(4, -1)$. Q is in Quadrant IV.

Exercises

Write the ordered pair for each point shown at the right. Name the quadrant in which the point is located.

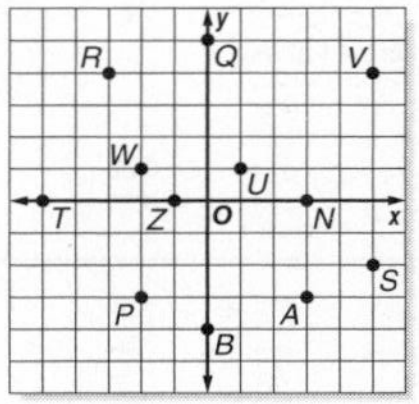

1. N (3, 0), none
2. P (-2, -3), III
3. Q (0, 5), none
4. R (-3, 4), II
5. S (5, -2), IV
6. T (-5, 0), none
7. U (1, 1), I
8. V (5, 4), I
9. W (-2, 1), II
10. Z (-1, 0), none
11. A (3, -3), IV
12. B (0, -4), none

13. Write the ordered pair that describes a point 4 units down from and 3 units to the right of the origin. (3, -4)

14. Write the ordered pair that is 8 units to the left of the origin and lies on the x-axis. (-8, 0)

4-1 Study Guide and Intervention (continued)

The Coordinate Plane

Graph Points To **graph** an ordered pair means to draw a dot at the point on the coordinate plane that corresponds to the ordered pair. To graph an ordered pair (x, y), begin at the origin. Move left or right x units. From there, move up or down y units. Draw a dot at that point.

Example Plot each point on a coordinate plane.

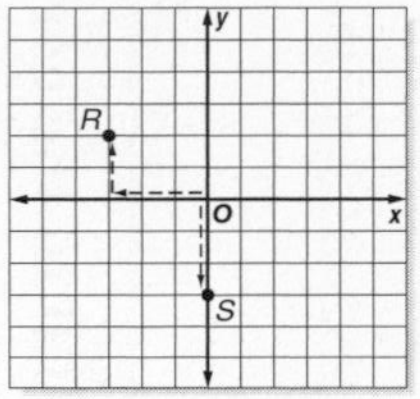

a. $R(-3, 2)$

Start at the origin. Move left 3 units since the x-coordinate is -3. Move up 2 units since the y-coordinate is 2. Draw a dot and label it R.

b. $S(0, -3)$

Start at the origin. Since the x-coordinate is 0, the point will be located on the y-axis. Move down 3 units since the y-coordinate is -3. Draw a dot and label it S.

Exercises

Plot each point on the coordinate plane at the right.   1–16. See graph.

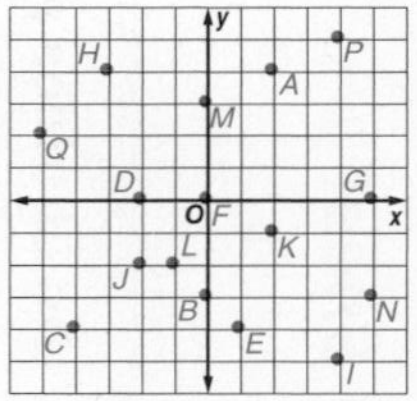

1. $A(2, 4)$
2. $B(0, -3)$
3. $C(-4, -4)$
4. $D(-2, 0)$
5. $E(1, -4)$
6. $F(0, 0)$
7. $G(5, 0)$
8. $H(-3, 4)$
9. $I(4, -5)$
10. $J(-2, -2)$
11. $K(2, -1)$
12. $L(-1, -2)$
13. $M(0, 3)$
14. $N(5, -3)$
15. $P(4, 5)$
16. $Q(-5, 2)$

Lesson 4-1

Practice (Average)
The Coordinate Plane

4-1

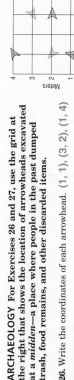

Write the ordered pair for each point shown at the right. Name the quadrant in which the point is located.

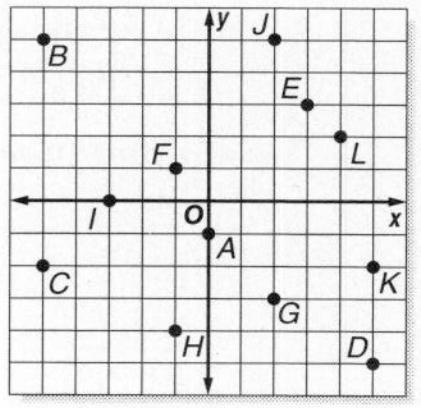

1. A (0, −1); none
2. B (−5, 5); II
3. C (−5, −2); III
4. D (5, −5); IV
5. E (3, 3); I
6. F (−1, 1); II
7. G (2, −3); IV
8. H (−1, −4); III
9. I (−3, 0); none
10. J (2, 5); I
11. K (5, −2); IV
12. L (4, 2); I

Plot each point on the coordinate plane at the right.

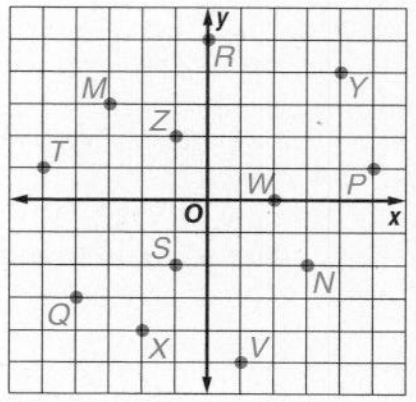

13. M(−3, 3)
14. N(3, −2)
15. P(5, 1)
16. Q(−4, −3)
17. R(0, 5)
18. S(−1, −2)
19. T(−5, 1)
20. V(1, −5)
21. W(2, 0)
22. X(−2, −4)
23. Y(4, 4)
24. Z(−1, 2)

25. **CHESS** Letters and numbers are used to show the positions of chess pieces and to describe their moves. For example, in the diagram at the right, a white pawn is located at f5. Name the positions of each of the remaining chess pieces.

white pawns: a7, c6; black pawns: b4, d7; white king: g3; black king: e8

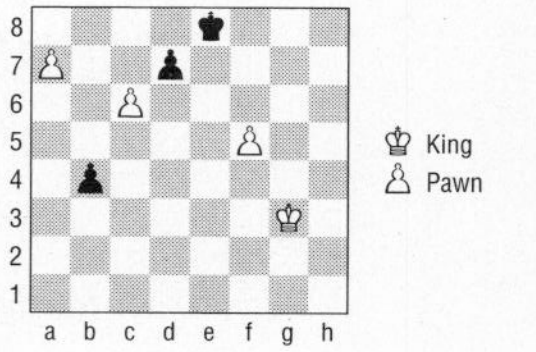

ARCHAEOLOGY For Exercises 26 and 27, use the grid at the right that shows the location of arrowheads excavated at a *midden*—a place where people in the past dumped trash, food remains, and other discarded items.

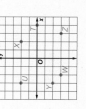

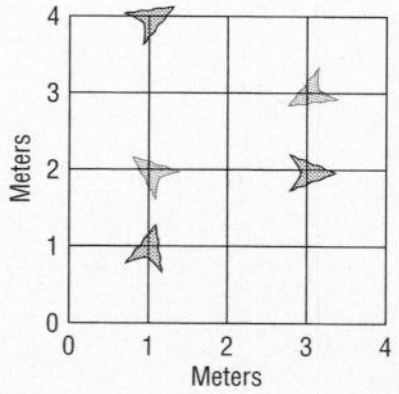

26. Write the coordinates of each arrowhead. (1, 1), (3, 2), (1, 4)

27. Suppose an archaeologist discovers two other arrowheads located at (1, 2) and (3, 3). Draw an arrowhead at each of these locations on the grid.

216 *Glencoe Algebra 1*

Lesson 4-1

Skills Practice
The Coordinate Plane

4-1

Write the ordered pair for each point shown at the right. Name the quadrant in which the point is located.

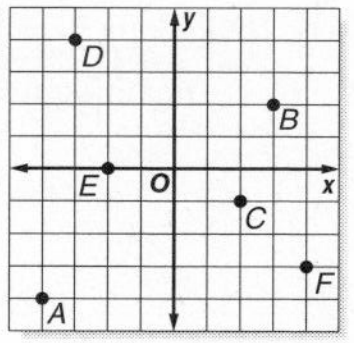

1. A (−4, −4); III
2. B (3, 2); I
3. C (2, −1); IV
4. D (−3, 4); II
5. E (−2, 0); none
6. F (4, −3); IV

Write the ordered pair for each point shown at the right. Name the quadrant in which the point is located.

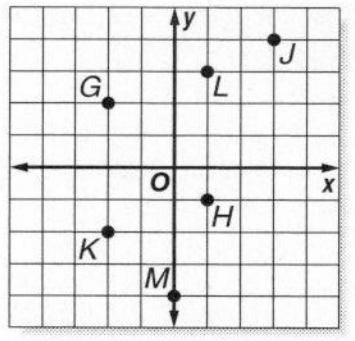

7. G (−2, 2); II
8. H (1, −1); IV
9. J (3, 4); I
10. K (−2, −2); III
11. L (1, 3); I
12. M (0, −4); none

Plot each point on the coordinate plane at the right.

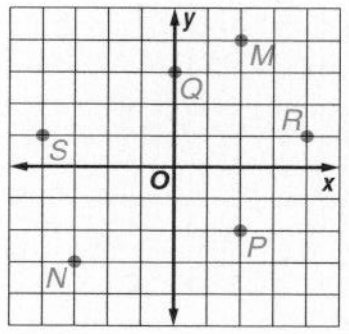

13. M(2, 4)
14. N(−3, −3)
15. P(2, −2)
16. Q(0, 3)
17. R(4, 1)
18. S(−4, 1)

Plot each point on the coordinate plane at the right.

19. T(4, 0)
20. U(−3, 2)
21. W(−2, −3)
22. X(2, 2)
23. Y(−3, −2)
24. Z(3, −3)

215 *Glencoe Algebra 1*

Answers

NAME _____ DATE _____ PERIOD _____

4-1 Enrichment

Midpoint

The *midpoint* of a line segment is the point that lies exactly halfway between the two endpoints of the segment. The coordinates of the midpoint of a line segment whose endpoints are (x_1, y_1) and (x_2, y_2) are given by $\left(\dfrac{x_1 + x_2}{2}, \dfrac{y_1 + y_2}{2}\right)$.

Find the midpoint of each line segment with the given endpoints.

1. $(7, 1)$ and $(-3, 1)$

    $(2, 1)$

2. $(5, -2)$ and $(9, -8)$

    $(7, -5)$

3. $(-4, 4)$ and $(4, -4)$

    $(0, 0)$

4. $(-3, -6)$ and $(-10, -15)$

    $(-6.5, -10.5)$

Plot each segment in the coordinate plane. Then find the coordinates of the midpoint.

5. $\overline{JK}$ with $J(5, 2)$ and $K(-2, -4)$

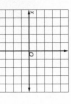

    $(1.5, -1)$

6. $\overline{PQ}$ with $P(-1, 4)$ and $Q(3, -1)$

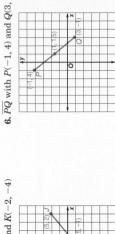

    $(1, 1.5)$

You are given the coordinates of one endpoint of a line segment and the midpoint M. Find the coordinates of the other endpoint.

7. $A(-10, 3)$ and $M(-6, 7)$

    $(-2, 11)$

8. $D(-1, 4)$ and $M(3, -6)$

    $(7, -16)$

© Glencoe/McGraw-Hill   218   *Glencoe Algebra 1*

Lesson 4-1

NAME _____ DATE _____ PERIOD _____

4-1 Reading to Learn Mathematics

The Coordinate Plane

Pre-Activity **How do archaeologists use coordinate systems?**

Read the introduction to Lesson 4-1 at the top of page 192 in your textbook. What do the terms *grid system*, *grid*, and *coordinate system* mean to you? **See students' work.**

Reading the Lesson

1. Use the coordinate plane shown at the right.

    a. Label the origin *O*.

    b. Label the *y*-axis *y*.

    c. Label the *x*-axis *x*.

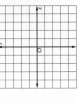

2. Explain why the coordinates of the origin are $(0, 0)$. **Sample answer: The origin is the intersection of two number lines at their common zero point.**

3. Use the ordered pair $(-2, 3)$.

    a. Explain how to identify the *x*- and *y*-coordinates. **The *x*-coordinate is the first number, the *y*-coordinate is the second number.**

    b. Name the *x*- and *y*-coordinates. **The *x*-coordinate is -2, the *y*-coordinate is 3.**

    c. Describe the steps you would use to locate the point for $(-2, 3)$ on the coordinate plane. **Start at the origin. Move left 2 units. Then move up 3 units.**

4. What does the term *quadrant* mean? **Sample answer: one of the four regions in the coordinate plane**

Helping You Remember

5. Explain how the way the axes are labeled on the coordinate plane can help you remember how to plot the point for an ordered pair. **Sample answer: The right side of the horizontal axis is labeled with the letter *x*. This is the side of the horizontal number line where you find positive numbers. The top end of the vertical number line is labeled with the letter *y*. This is the part of the vertical number line where you find positive numbers.**

© Glencoe/McGraw-Hill   217   *Glencoe Algebra 1*

Answers (Lesson 4-2)

Left page

NAME _____ DATE _____ PERIOD _____

4-2 Study Guide and Intervention

Transformations on the Coordinate Plane

Transform Figures Transformations are movements of geometric figures. The **preimage** is the position of the figure before the transformation, and the **image** is the position of the figure after the transformation.

Reflection	A figure is flipped over a line.
Translation	A figure is slid horizontally, vertically, or both.
Dilation	A figure is enlarged or reduced.
Rotation	A figure is turned around a point.

Example **Determine whether each transformation is a *reflection, translation, dilation, or rotation*.**

a. The figure has been flipped over a line, so this is a reflection.

b. The figure has been turned around a point, so this is a rotation.

c. The figure has been reduced in size, so this is a dilation.

d. The figure has been shifted horizontally to the right, so this is a translation.

Exercises

Determine whether each transformation is a *reflection, translation, dilation, or rotation*.

1. reflection
2. dilation
3. rotation
4. translation
5. dilation
6. rotation

219 © Glencoe/McGraw-Hill   *Glencoe Algebra 1*

Right page

NAME _____ DATE _____ PERIOD _____

4-2 Study Guide and Intervention *(continued)*

Transformations on the Coordinate Plane

Transform Figures on the Coordinate Plane You can perform transformations on a coordinate plane by changing the coordinates of each vertex. The vertices of the image of the transformed figure are indicated by the symbol ′, which is read *prime*.

Reflection over x-axis	$(x, y) \rightarrow (x, -y)$
Reflection over y-axis	$(x, y) \rightarrow (-x, y)$
Translation	$(x, y) \rightarrow (x + a, y + b)$
Dilation	$(x, y) \rightarrow (kx, ky)$
Rotation 90° counterclockwise	$(x, y) \rightarrow (-y, x)$
Rotation 180°	$(x, y) \rightarrow (-x, -y)$

Example **A triangle has vertices $A(-1, 1)$, $B(2, 4)$, and $C(3, 0)$. Find the coordinates of the vertices of each image below.**

a. **reflection over the x-axis**

To reflect a point over the x-axis, multiply the y-coordinate by −1.

$A(-1, 1) \rightarrow A'(-1, -1)$
$B(2, 4) \rightarrow B'(2, -4)$
$C(3, 0) \rightarrow C'(3, 0)$

The coordinates of the image vertices are $A'(-1, -1)$, $B'(2, -4)$, and $C'(3, 0)$.

b. **dilation with a scale factor of 2**

Find the coordinates of the dilated figure by multiplying the coordinates by 2.

$A(-1, 1) \rightarrow A'(-2, 2)$
$B(2, 4) \rightarrow B'(4, 8)$
$C(3, 0) \rightarrow C'(6, 0)$

The coordinates of the image vertices are $A'(-2, 2)$, $B'(4, 8)$, and $C''(6, 0)$.

Exercises

Find the coordinates of the vertices of each figure after the given transformation is performed.

1. triangle *RST* with $R(-2, 4)$, $S(2, 0)$, $T(-1, -1)$ reflected over the y-axis
$R'(2, 4)$, $S'(-2, 0)$, $T'(1, -1)$

2. triangle *ABC* with $A(0, 0)$, $B(2, 4)$, $C(3, 0)$ rotated about the origin 180°
$A'(0, 0)$, $B'(-2, -4)$, $C'(-3, 0)$

3. parallelogram *ABCD* with $A(-3, 0)$, $B(-2, 3)$, $C(3, 3)$, $D(2, 0)$ translated 3 units down
$A'(-3, -3)$, $B'(-2, 0)$, $C'(3, 0)$, $D'(2, -3)$

4. quadrilateral *RSTU* with $R(-2, 2)$, $S(2, 4)$, $T(4, 4)$, $U(4, 0)$ dilated by a factor of $\frac{1}{2}$
$R'(-1, 1)$, $S'(1, 2)$, $T'(2, 2)$, $U'(2, 0)$

5. triangle *ABC* with $A(-4, 0)$, $B(-2, 3)$, $C(0, 0)$ rotated counterclockwise 90°
$A'(0, -4)$, $B'(-3, -2)$, $C'(0, 0)$

6. hexagon *ABCDEF* with $A(0, 0)$, $B(-2, 3)$, $C(0, 4)$, $D(3, 4)$, $E(4, 2)$, $F(3, 0)$ translated 2 units up and 1 unit to the left
$A'(-1, 2)$, $B'(-3, 5)$, $C'(-1, 6)$, $D'(2, 6)$, $E'(3, 4)$, $F'(2, 2)$

220 © Glencoe/McGraw-Hill   *Glencoe Algebra 1*

Lesson 4-2

Answers (Lesson 4-2)

4-2 Skills Practice

Transformations on the Coordinate Plane

Identify each transformation as a *reflection, translation, dilation,* or *rotation.*

1.

   rotation

2.

   reflection

3.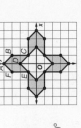

   translation

4.

   dilation

5.

   reflection

6.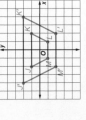

   rotation

For Exercises 7–10, complete parts a and b.

a. Find the coordinates of the vertices of each figure after the given transformation is performed.

b. Graph the preimage and its image.

7. triangle *ABC* with *A*(1, 2), *B*(4, −1), and *C*(1, −1) reflected over the *y*-axis
   A′(−1, 2), *B′*(−4, −1), and *C′*(−1, −1)

8. parallelogram *PQRS* with *P*(−2, −1), *Q*(3, −1), *R*(2, −3), and *S*(−3, −3) translated 3 units up *P′*(−2, 2), *Q′*(3, 2), *R′*(2, 0), and *S′*(−3, 0)

9. trapezoid *JKLM* with *J*(−2, 1), *K*(2, 1), *L*(1, −1), and *M*(−1, −1) dilated by a scale factor of 2 *J′*(−4, 2), *K′*(4, 2), *L′*(2, −2), and *M′*(−2, −2)

10. triangle *STU* with *S*(3, 3), *T*(5, 1), and *U*(1, 1) rotated 90° counterclockwise about the origin
    S′(−3, 3), *T′*(−1, 5), *U′*(−1, 1)

221

Glencoe Algebra 1

4-2 Practice (Average)

Transformations on the Coordinate Plane

Identify each transformation as a *reflection, translation, dilation,* or *rotation.*

1.

   reflection

2. translation

3. rotation

For Exercises 4–6, complete parts a and b.

a. Find the coordinates of the vertices of each figure after the given transformation is performed.

b. Graph the preimage and its image.

4. triangle *DEF* with *D*(2, 3), *E*(4, 1), and *F*(1, −1) translated 4 units left and 3 units down
   D′(−2, 0), *E′*(0, −2), *F′*(−3, −4)

5. trapezoid *EFGH* with *E*(3, 2), *F*(3, −3), *G*(1, −2), and *H*(1, 1) reflected over the *y*-axis
   E′(−3, 2), *F′*(−3, −3), *G′*(−1, −2), *H′*(−1, 1)

6. triangle *XYZ* with *X*(3, 1), *Y*(4, −2), and *Z*(1, −3) rotated 90° counterclockwise about the origin
   X′(−1, 3), *Y′*(2, 4), *Z′*(3, 1)

GRAPHICS For Exercises 7–9, use the diagram at the right and the following information.

A designer wants to dilate the rocket by a scale factor of $\frac{1}{2}$, and then translate it $5\frac{1}{2}$ units up.

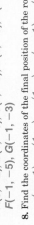

7. Write the coordinates for the vertices of the rocket.
   A(0, −2), *B*(1, −3), *C*(1, −5), *D*(2, −6), *E*(−2, −6), *F*(−1, −5), *G*(−1, −3)

8. Find the coordinates of the final position of the rocket.
   A′(0, 4½), *B′*(½, 4), *C′*(½, 3), *D′*(1, 2½), *E′*(−1, 2½), *F′*(−½, 3), *G′*(−½, 4)

9. Graph the image on the coordinate plane.

10. **DESIGN** Ramona transformed figure *ABCDEF* to design a pattern for a quilt. Name two different sets of transformations she could have used to design the pattern. **Sample answer:** reflection over the *x*-axis, 90° counterclockwise rotation, and then reflection over the *y*-axis; three 90° counterclockwise rotations

222

Glencoe Algebra 1

Lesson 4-2

Left Worksheet

© Glencoe/McGraw-Hill

NAME _____ DATE _____ PERIOD _____

4-2 Reading to Learn Mathematics

Transformations on the Coordinate Plane

Pre-Activity **How are transformations used in computer graphics?**

Read the introduction to Lesson 4-2 at the top of page 197 in your textbook.

In the sentence, "Computer graphic designers can create movement that mimics real-life situations," what phrase indicates the use of transformations? **create movement**

Reading the Lesson

1. Suppose you look at a diagram that shows two figures *ABCDE* and *A'B'C'DE'*. If one figure was obtained from the other by using a transformation, how do you tell which was the original figure? **The letters that have no prime symbols are used for vertices of the original figure.**

2. Write the letter of the term and the Roman numeral of the figure that best matches each statement.

a. A figure is flipped over a line. **C, I**   **A.** dilation   **I.**

b. A figure is turned around a point. **D, III**   **B.** translation   **II.**

c. A figure is enlarged or reduced. **A, II**   **C.** reflection   **III.**

d. A figure is slid horizontally, vertically, or both. **B, IV**   **D.** rotation   **IV.**

Helping You Remember

3. Give examples of things in everyday life that can help you remember what reflections, dilations, and rotations are. **Sample answer: For a reflection, think of looking at yourself in a mirror. For a dilation, think of how your hand looks if you hold it far from your face and then move it straight in, very close to your face. For a rotation, think of twisting the top of a jar to open the jar.**

223

Glencoe Algebra 1

Lesson 4-2

Right Worksheet

NAME _____ DATE _____ PERIOD _____

4-2 Enrichment

The Legendary City of Ur

The city of Ur was founded more than five thousand years ago in Mesopotamia (modern-day Iraq). It was one of the world's first cities. Between 1922 and 1934, archeologists discovered many treasures from this ancient city. A large cemetery from the 26th century B.C. was found to contain large quantities of gold, silver, bronze, and jewels. The many cultural artifacts that were found, such as musical instruments, weapons, mosaics, and statues, have provided historians with valuable clues about the civilization that existed in early Mesopotamia.

1. Suppose that the ordered pairs below represent the volume (cm³) and mass (grams) of ten artifacts from the city of Ur. Plot each point on the graph.

A(10, 150)
B(150, 1350)
C(200, 1760)
D(50, 525)
E(100, 1500)
F(10, 88)
G(200, 2100)
H(150, 1675)
I(100, 900)
J(50, 440)

2. The equation relating mass, density, and volume for silver is $m = 10.5V$. Which of the points in Exercise 1 are solutions for this equation?

D* and *G

3. Suppose that the equation $m = 8.8V$ relates mass, density, and volume for the kind of bronze used in the ancient city of Ur. Which of the points in Exercise 1 are solutions for this equation?

C, F, J

4. Explain why the graph in Exercise 1 shows only quadrant 1. **Neither the mass nor the volume can be a negative number.**

224

Glencoe Algebra 1

© Glencoe/McGraw-Hill

Answers

4-3 Study Guide and Intervention (continued)
Relations

Inverse Relations The inverse of any relation is obtained by switching the coordinates in each ordered pair.

Example Express the relation shown in the mapping as a set of ordered pairs. Then write the inverse of the relation.

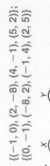

Relation: {(6, 5), (2, 3), (1, 4), (0, 3)}
Inverse: {(5, 6), (3, 2), (4, 1), (3, 0)}

Exercises
Express the relation shown in each table, mapping, or graph as a set of ordered pairs. Then write the inverse of each relation.

1.

x	y
-2	4
-1	3
2	1
4	5

{(-2, 4), (-1, 3), (2, 1), (4, 5)};
{(4, -2), (3, -1), (1, 2), (5, 4)}

2.

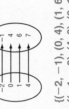

{(-1, 0), (2, -8), (4, -1), (5, 2)};
{(0, -1), (-8, 2), (-1, 4), (2, 5)}

3.

x	y
-3	5
-2	-1
1	0
2	4

{(-3, 5), (-2, -1), (1, 0), (2, 4)};
{(5, -3), (-1, -2), (0, 1), (4, 2)}

4.

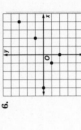

{(-2, -1), (0, 4), (1, 6), (4, 7)};
{(-1, -2), (4, 0), (6, 1), (7, 4)}

5.

{(-2, 2), (1, -2), (2, 4), (3, 0)};
{(2, -2), (-2, 1), (4, 2), (0, 3)}

6.

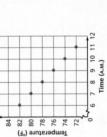

{(-4, 0), (-1, -1), (0, -2), (2, 1), (4, 3)};
{(0, -4), (-1, -1), (-2, 0), (1, 2), (3, 4)}

Lesson 4-3

4-3 Study Guide and Intervention
Relations

Represent Relations A relation is a set of ordered pairs. A relation can be represented by a set of ordered pairs, a table, a graph, or a **mapping**. A mapping illustrates how each element of the domain is paired with an element in the range.

Example 1 Express the relation {(1, 1), (0, 2), (3, -2)} as a table, a graph, and a mapping. State the domain and range of the relation.

x	y
1	1
0	2
3	-2

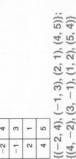

The domain for this relation is {0, 1, 3}.
The range for this relation is {-2, 1, 2}.

Example 2 A person playing racquetball uses 4 calories per hour for every pound he or she weighs.

a. Make a table to show the relation between weight and calories burned in one hour for people weighing 100, 110, 120, and 130 pounds.
Source: The Math Teacher's Book of Lists

x	y
100	400
110	440
120	480
130	520

b. Give the domain and range.
domain: {100, 110, 120, 130}
range: {400, 440, 480, 520}

c. Graph the relation.

Exercises

1. Express the relation {(-2, -1), (3, 3), (4, 3)} as a table, a graph, and a mapping. Then determine the domain and range.

x	y
-2	-1
3	3
4	3

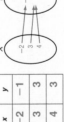

domain: {-2, 3, 4};
range: {-1, 3}

2. The temperature in a house drops 2° for every hour the air conditioner is on between the hours of 6 A.M. and 11 A.M. Make a graph to show the relationship between time and temperature if the temperature at 6 A.M. was 82°F.

Answers (Lesson 4-3)

Skills Practice (page 227)

NAME _____ DATE _____ PERIOD _____

4-3 Skills Practice
Relations

Express each relation as a table, a graph, and a mapping. Then determine the domain and range.

1. {(−1, −1), (1, 1), (2, 1), (3, 2)}

x	y
−1	−1
1	1
2	1
3	2

D = {−1, 1, 2, 3}; R = {−1, 1, 2}

2. {(0, 4), (−4, −4), (−2, 3), (4, 0)}

x	y
0	4
−4	−4
−2	3
4	0

D = {−4, −2, 0, 4}; R = {−4, 0, 3, 4}

3. {(3, −2), (1, 0), (−2, 4), (3, 1)}

x	y
3	−2
1	0
−2	4
3	1

D = {−2, 1, 3}; R = {−2, 0, 1, 4}

Express the relation shown in each table, mapping, or graph as a set of ordered pairs. Then write the inverse of the relation.

4.

x	y
3	−5
−4	3
7	6
1	−2

{(3, −5), (−4, 3), (7, 6), (1, −2)}; {(−5, 3), (3, −4), (6, 7), (−2, 1)}

5. {(9, 7), (−5, 6), (4, 8), (4, 2)}; {(7, 9), (6, −5), (8, 4), (2, 4)}

6. {(−3, 1), (−3, 2), (3, 1), (3, −3)}; {(1, −3), (2, −3), (1, 3), (−3, 3)}

© Glencoe/McGraw-Hill   227   Glencoe Algebra 1

Practice (Average) (page 228)

NAME _____ DATE _____ PERIOD _____

4-3 Practice (Average)
Relations

Express each relation as a table, a graph, and a mapping. Then determine the domain and range.

1. {(4, 3), (−1, 4), (3, −2), (2, 3), (−2, 1)}

x	y
4	3
−1	4
3	−2
2	3
−2	1

D = {−2, −1, 2, 3, 4}; R = {−2, 1, 3, 4}

Express the relation shown in each table, mapping, or graph as a set of ordered pairs. Then write the inverse of the relation.

2.

x	y
0	9
−8	3
9	−6
1	4

{(0, 9), (−8, 3), (9, −6), (1, 4)}; {(9, 0), (3, −8), (−6, 9), (4, 1)}

3. {(9, 5), (9, 3), (−6, −5), (4, 3), (8, −5), (8, 7)}; {(5, 9), (3, 9), (−5, −6), (3, 4), (−5, 8), (7, 8)}

4. {(−3, −1), (−2, −2), (−1, −3), (1, 1), (2, 1), (3, 1)}; {(−1, −3), (−2, −2), (−3, −1), (1, 1), (1, 2), (1, 3)}

BASEBALL For Exercises 5 and 6, use the graph that shows the batting average for Barry Bonds of the San Francisco Giants. Source: www.sportsillustrated.cnn.com

Barry Bonds' Batting Average

5. Find the domain and estimate the range.
D = {1996, 1997, 1998, 1999, 2000, 2001};
R = {.262, .291, .303, .306, .308, .328}

6. Which seasons did Bonds have the lowest and highest batting averages? lowest: 1999, highest: 2001

METEORS For Exercises 7 and 8, use the table that shows the number of meteors Ann observed each hour during a meteor shower.

Meteor Shower

Time (A.M.)	Number of Meteors
12	15
1	26
2	28
3	28
4	15

7. What are the domain and range?
D = {12, 1, 2, 3, 4}; R = {15, 26, 28}

8. Graph the relation.

© Glencoe/McGraw-Hill   228   Glencoe Algebra 1

4-3 Enrichment

Inverse Relations

On each grid below, plot the points in Sets A and B. Then connect the points in Set A with the corresponding points in Set B. Then find the inverses of Set A and Set B, plot the two sets, and connect those points.

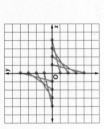

Set A	Set B
(−4, 0)	(0, 1)
(−3, 0)	(0, 2)
(−2, 0)	(0, 3)
(−1, 0)	(0, 4)

Inverse

	Set A	Set B
1.	(0, −4)	(1, 0)
2.	(0, −3)	(2, 0)
3.	(0, −2)	(3, 0)
4.	(0, −1)	(4, 0)

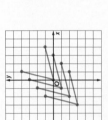

Set A	Set B
(−3, −3)	(−2, 1)
(−2, −2)	(−1, 2)
(−1, −1)	(0, 3)
(0, 0)	(1, 4)

Inverse

	Set A	Set B
5.	(−3, −3)	(1, −2)
6.	(−2, −2)	(2, −1)
7.	(−1, −1)	(3, 0)
8.	(0, 0)	(4, 1)

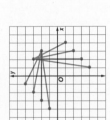

Set A	Set B
(−4, 1)	(3, 2)
(−3, 2)	(3, 2)
(−2, 3)	(3, 2)
(−1, 4)	(3, 2)

Inverse

	Set A	Set B
9.	(1, −4)	(2, 3)
10.	(2, −3)	(2, 3)
11.	(3, −2)	(2, 3)
12.	(4, −1)	(2, 3)

13. What is the graphical relationship between the line segments you drew connecting points in Sets A and B and the line segments connecting points in the inverses of those two sets?

Answers will vary. A possible answer is that the graphs are reflected across the line $y = x$ by their inverses.

Lesson 4-3

4-3 Reading to Learn Mathematics

Relations

Pre-Activity **How can relations be used to represent baseball statistics?**

Read the introduction to Lesson 4-3 at the top of page 205 in your textbook.

In 1997, Ken Griffey, Jr. had __56__ home runs and __121__ strikeouts.

This can be represented with the ordered pair (__56__ , __121__).

Reading the Lesson

1. Look at page 205 in your textbook. There you see the same relation represented by a set of ordered pairs, a table, a graph, and a mapping.

a. In the list of ordered pairs, where do you see the numbers for the domain? the numbers for the range? before the commas; after the commas

b. What parts of the table show the domain and the range? The column of numbers under the letter *x* shows the domain, and the column of numbers under the letter *y* shows the range.

c. How do the table, the graph, and the mapping show that there are three ordered pairs in the relation? The table has three rows of numbers, the graph shows three points marked with dots, and the mapping uses three arrows.

2. Which tells you more about a relation, a list of the ordered pairs in the relation or the domain and range of the relation? Explain. **Sample answer: A list of the ordered pairs tells you more.** You can use it to find the domain and the range, and you know exactly how the numbers are paired. If you only know the domain and the range, you cannot be sure how the numbers are paired.

3. Describe how you would find the inverse of the relation ((1, 2), (2, 4), (3, 6), (4, 8)). Switch the coordinates in each ordered pair to get {(2, 1), (4, 2), (6, 3), (8, 4)}.

Helping You Remember

4. The first letters in two words and their order in the alphabet can sometimes help you remember their mathematical meaning. Two key terms in this lesson are *domain* and *range*. Describe how the alphabet method could help you remember their meaning. **Sample answer:** *d* comes first for the first coordinate, *r* comes second for the second coordinate.

Page 231 (Lesson 4-4)

4-4 Study Guide and Intervention
Equations as Relations

Solve Equations The equation $y = 3x - 4$ is an example of an **equation in two variables** because it contains two variables, x and y. The **solution** of an equation in two variables is an ordered pair of replacements for the variables that results in a true statement when substituted into the equation.

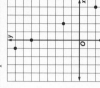

Example 1 **Find the solution set for $y = -2x - 1$, given the replacement set $\{(-2, 3), (0, -1), (1, -2), (3, 1)\}$.**

Make a table. Substitute the x and y-values of each ordered pair into the equation.

x	y	$y = -2x - 1$	True or False
-2	3	$3 = -2(-2) - 1$ $3 = 3$	True
0	-1	$-1 = -2(0) - 1$ $-1 = -1$	True
1	-2	$-2 = -2(1) - 1$ $-2 = -3$	False
3	1	$1 = -2(3) - 1$ $1 = -7$	False

The ordered pairs $(-2, 3)$, and $(0, -1)$ result in true statements. The solution set is $\{(-2, 3), (0, -1)\}$.

Example 2 **Solve $b = 2a - 1$ if the domain is $\{-2, -1, 0, 2, 4\}$.**

Make a table. The values of a come from the domain. Substitute each value of a into the equation to determine the corresponding values of b in the range.

a	$2a - 1$	b	(a, b)
-2	$2(-2) - 1$	-5	$(-2, -5)$
-1	$2(-1) - 1$	-3	$(-1, -3)$
0	$2(0) - 1$	-1	$(0, -1)$
2	$2(2) - 1$	3	$(2, 3)$
4	$2(4) - 1$	7	$(4, 7)$

The solution set is $\{(-2, -5), (-1, -3), (0, -1), (2, 3), (4, 7)\}$.

Exercises

Find the solution set of each equation, given the replacement set.

1. $y = 3x + 1$; $\{(0, 1), (\frac{1}{3}, 2), (-1, -\frac{2}{3}), (-1, -2)\}$ $\{(0, 1), (\frac{1}{3}, 2), (-1, -2)\}$

2. $3x - 2y = 6$; $\{(-2, 3), (0, 1), (0, -3), (2, 0)\}$ $\{(0, -3), (2, 0)\}$

3. $2x = 5 - y$; $\{(1, 3), (2, 1), (3, 2), (4, 3)\}$ $\{(1, 3), (2, 1)\}$

Solve each equation if the domain is $\{-4, -2, 0, 2, 4\}$.

4. $x + y = 4$ $\{(-4, 8), (-2, 6), (0, 4), (2, 2) (4, 0)\}$

5. $y = -4x - 6$ $\{(-4, 10), (-2, 2), (0, -6), (2, -14), (4, -22)\}$

6. $5a - 2b = 10$ $\{(-4, -15), (-2, -10), (0, -5), (2, 0), (4, 5)\}$

7. $3x - 2y = 12$ $\{(-4, -12), (-2, -9), (0, -6), (2, -3) (4, 0)\}$

8. $6x + 3y = 18$ $\{(-4, 14), (-2, 10), (0, 6), (2, 2), (4, -2)\}$

9. $4x + 8 = 2y$ $\{(-4, -4), (-2, 0), (0, 4), (2, 8), (4, 12)\}$

10. $x - y = 8$ $\{(-4, -12), (-2, -10), (0, -8), (2, -6) (4, -4)\}$

11. $2x + y = 10$ $\{(-4, 18), (-2, 14), (0, 10), (2, 6), (4, 2)\}$

Page 232 (Lesson 4-4)

4-4 Study Guide and Intervention (continued)
Equations as Relations

Graph Solution Sets You can graph the ordered pairs in the solution set of an equation in two variables. The domain contains values represented by the **independent variable**. The range contains the corresponding values represented by the **dependent variable**, which are determined by the given equation.

Example **Solve $4x + 2y = 12$ if the domain is $\{-1, 0, 2, 4\}$. Graph the solution set.**

First solve the equation for y in terms of x.

$4x + 2y = 12$ Original equation
$4x + 2y - 4x = 12 - 4x$ Subtract $4x$ from each side.
$2y = 12 - 4x$ Simplify.
$\frac{2y}{2} = \frac{12 - 4x}{2}$ Divide each side by 2.
$y = 6 - 2x$ Simplify.

Substitute each value of x from the domain to determine the corresponding value of y in the range.

x	6 − 2x	y	(x, y)
-1	$6 - 2(-1)$	8	$(-1, 8)$
0	$6 - 2(0)$	6	$(0, 6)$
2	$6 - 2(2)$	2	$(2, 2)$
4	$6 - 2(4)$	-2	$(4, -2)$

Graph the solution set.

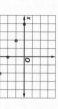

Exercises

Solve each equation for the given domain. Graph the solution set.

1. $x + 2y = 4$ for $x = \{-2, 0, 2, 4\}$

$\{(-2, 3), (0, 2), (2, 1), (4, 0)\}$

2. $y = -2x - 3$ for $x = \{-2, -1, 0, 1\}$

$\{(-2, 1), (-1, -1), (0, -3), (1, -5)\}$

3. $x - 3y = 6$ for $x = \{-3, 0, 3, 6\}$

$\{(-3, -3), (0, -2), (3, -1), (6, 0)\}$

4. $2x - 4y = 8$ for $x = \{-4, -2, 0, 2\}$

$\{(-4, -4), (-2, -3), (0, -2), (2, -1)\}$

Answers

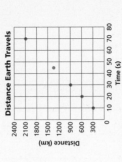

Top section

NAME _____ DATE _____ PERIOD _____

4-4 **Practice** (Average)

Equations as Relations

Find the solution set for each equation, given the replacement set.

1. $y = 2 - 5x$; $\{(3, 12), (-3, -17), (2, -8), (-1, 7)\}$ $\{(2, -8), (-1, 7)\}$

2. $3x - 2y = -1$; $\{(-1, 1), (-2, -2.5), (-1, -1.5), (0, 0.5)\}$ $\{(-2, -2.5), (0, 0.5)\}$

Solve each equation if the domain is $\{-2, -1, 2, 3, 5\}$.

3. $y = 4 - 2x$ $\{(-2, 8), (-1, 6), (2, 0), (3, -2), (5, -6)\}$

4. $x = 8 - y$ $\{(-2, 10), (-1, 9), (2, 6), (3, 5), (5, 3)\}$

5. $4x + 2y = 10$ $\{(-2, 9), (-1, 7), (2, 1), (3, -1), (5, -5)\}$

6. $3x - 6y = 12$ $\{(-2, -3), (-1, -2.5), (2, -1), (3, -0.5), (5, 0.5)\}$

7. $2x + 4y = 16$ $\{(-2, 5), (-1, 4.5), (2, 3), (3, 2.5), (5, 1.5)\}$

8. $x - \frac{1}{2}y = 6$ $\{(-2, -16), (-1, -14), (2, -8), (3, -6), (5, -2)\}$

Solve each equation for the given domain. Graph the solution set.

9. $2x - 4y = 8$ for $x = \{-4, -3, -2, 2, 5\}$

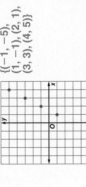

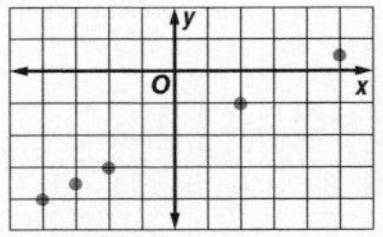

$\{(-4, -4),$
$(-3, -3.5),$
$(-2, -3),$
$(2, -1), (5, 0.5)\}$

10. $\frac{1}{2}x + y = 1$ for $x = \{-4, -3, -2, 0, 4\}$

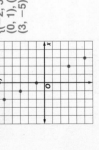

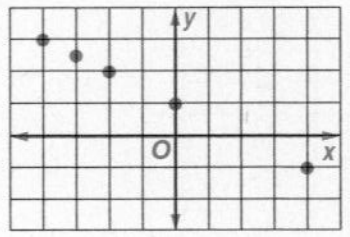

$\{(-4, 3), \left(-3, 2\frac{1}{2}\right),$
$(-2, 2), (0, 1),$
$(4, -1)\}$

EARTH SCIENCE For Exercises 11 and 12, use the following information.
Earth moves at a rate of 30 kilometers per second around the Sun. The equation $d = 30t$ relates the distance d in kilometers Earth moves to time t in seconds.

11. Find the set of ordered pairs when $t = \{10, 20, 30, 45, 70\}$. $\{(10, 300), (20, 600), (30, 900), (45, 1350), (70, 2100)\}$

12. Graph the set of ordered pairs.

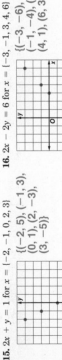

Distance Earth Travels

GEOMETRY For Exercises 13-15, use the following information.
The equation for the area of a triangle is $A = \frac{1}{2}bh$. Suppose the area of triangle DEF is 30 square inches.

13. Solve the equation for h. $h = \frac{60}{b}$

14. State the independent and dependent variables. b is independent; h is dependent.

15. Choose 5 values for b and find the corresponding values for h. Sample answer: $\{(5, 12), (6, 10), (10, 6), (12, 5), (15, 4)\}$

© Glencoe/McGraw-Hill 234 Glencoe Algebra 1

Lesson 4-4

Bottom section

NAME _____ DATE _____ PERIOD _____

4-4 **Skills Practice**

Equations as Relations

Find the solution set for each equation, given the replacement set.

1. $y = 3x - 1$; $\{(2, 5), (-2, 7), (0, -1), (1, 1)\}$ $\{(2, 5), (0, -1)\}$

2. $y = 2x + 4$; $\{(-1, -2), (-3, 2), (1, 6), (-2, 8)\}$ $\{(1, 6)\}$

3. $y = 7 - 2x$; $\{(3, 1), (4, -1), (5, -3), (-1, 5)\}$ $\{(3, 1), (4, -1), (5, -3)\}$

4. $-3x + y = 2$; $\{(-3, 7), (-2, -4), (-1, -1), (3, 11)\}$ $\{(-2, -4), (-1, -1), (3, 11)\}$

Solve each equation if the domain is $\{-2, -1, 0, 2, 5\}$.

5. $y = x + 4$ $\{(-2, 2), (-1, 3), (0, 4), (2, 6), (5, 9)\}$

6. $y = 3x - 2$ $\{(-2, -8), (-1, -5), (0, -2), (2, 4), (5, 13)\}$

7. $y = 2x + 1$ $\{(-2, -3), (-1, -1), (0, 1), (2, 5), (5, 11)\}$

8. $x = y + 2$ $\{(-2, -4), (-1, -3), (0, -2), (2, 0), (5, 3)\}$

9. $x = 3 - y$ $\{(-2, 5), (-1, 4), (0, 3), (2, 1), (5, -2)\}$

10. $2x + y = 4$ $\{(-2, 8), (-1, 6), (0, 4), (2, 0), (5, -6)\}$

11. $2x - y = 7$ $\{(-2, -11), (-1, -9), (0, -7), (2, -3), (5, 3)\}$

12. $4x + 2y = 6$ $\{(-2, 7), (-1, 5), (0, 3), (2, -1), (5, -7)\}$

Solve each equation for the given domain. Graph the solution set.

13. $y = 2x + 5$ for $x = \{-5, -4, -2, -1, 0\}$

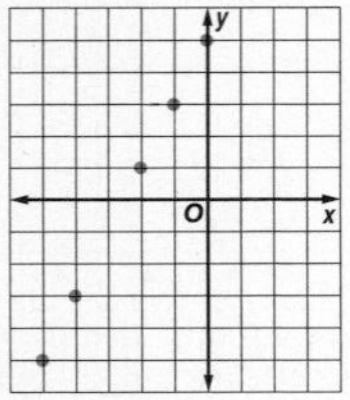

$\{(-5, -5),$
$(-4, -3),$
$(-2, 1), (-1, 3),$
$(0, 5)\}$

14. $y = 2x - 3$ for $x = \{-1, 1, 2, 3, 4\}$

$\{(-1, -5),$
$(1, -1), (2, 1),$
$(3, 3), (4, 5)\}$

15. $2x + y = 1$ for $x = \{-2, -1, 0, 2, 3\}$

$\{(-2, 5), (-1, 3),$
$(0, 1), (2, -3),$
$(3, -5)\}$

16. $2x - 2y = 6$ for $x = \{-3, -1, 3, 4, 6\}$

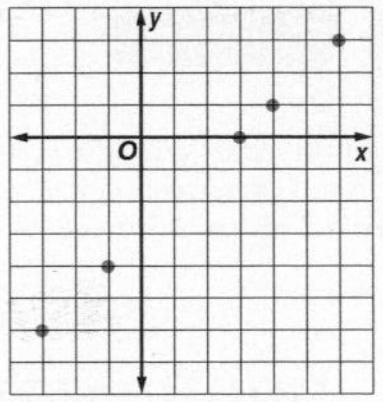

$\{(-3, -6),$
$(-1, -4), (3, 0),$
$(4, 1), (6, 3)\}$

© Glencoe/McGraw-Hill 233 Glencoe Algebra 1

4-4 Reading to Learn Mathematics

Equations as Relations

Pre-Activity **Why are equations of relations important in traveling?**

Read the introduction to Lesson 4-4 at the top of page 212 in your textbook.

- In the equation $p = 0.69d$, p represents **pounds** and d represents **dollars**.

- How many variables are in the equation $p = 0.69d$? **two**

Reading the Lesson

1. Suppose you make the following table to solve an equation that uses the domain $\{-3, -2, -1, 0, 1\}$.

x	x − 4	y	(x, y)
−3	−3 − 4	−7	(−3, −7)
−2	−2 − 4	−6	(−2, −6)
−1	−1 − 4	−5	(−1, −5)
0	0 − 4	−4	(0, −4)
1	1 − 4	−3	(1, −3)

a. What is the equation? $y = x - 4$

b. Which column shows the *domain*? **the first column**

c. Which column shows the *range*? **the third column**

d. Which column shows the *solution set*? **the fourth column**

2. The solution set of the equation $y = 2x$ for a given domain is $\{(-2, -4), (0, 0), (2, 4), (7, 14)\}$. Tell whether each sentence is *true* or *false*. If false, replace the underlined word(s) to make a true sentence.

a. The domain contains the values represented by the independent variable. **true**

b. The <u>domain</u> contains the numbers −4, 0, 4, and 14. **false; range**

c. For each number in the domain, the range contains a corresponding number that is a value of the dependent variable. **true**

3. What is meant by "solving an equation for y in terms of x"? **isolating y on one side of the equation**

Helping You Remember

4. Remember, *when you solve an equation for a given variable, that variable becomes the dependent variable.* Write an equation and describe how you would identify the dependent variable. **Sample answer: $y = 3x$ shows that you have solved for y, so y is the dependent variable.**

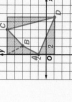

4-4 Enrichment

Coordinate Geometry and Area

How would you find the area of a triangle whose vertices have the coordinates $A(-1, 2)$, $B(1, 4)$, and $C(3, 0)$?

When a figure has no sides parallel to either axis, the height and base are difficult to find.

One method of finding the area is to enclose the figure in a rectangle and subtract the area of the surrounding triangles from the area of the rectangle.

Area of rectangle *DEFC*
$= 4 \times 4$
$= 16$ square units

Area of triangle I $= \frac{1}{2}(2)(4) = 4$

Area of triangle II $= \frac{1}{2}(2)(4) = 4$

Area of triangle III $= \frac{1}{2}(2)(2) = 2$

Total $= 10$ square units

Area of triangle $ABC = 16 - 10$, or 6 square units

Find the areas of the figures with the following vertices.

1. $A(-4, -6)$, $B(0, 4)$, $C(4, 2)$

24 square units

2. $A(6, -2)$, $B(8, -10)$, $C(12, -6)$

20 square units

3. $A(0, 2)$, $B(2, 7)$, $C(6, 10)$, $D(9, -2)$

55 square units

Answers

NAME _____ DATE _____ PERIOD _____

4-5 Study Guide and Intervention
Graphing Linear Equations

Identify Linear Equations A linear equation is an equation that can be written in the form $Ax + By = C$. This is called the **standard form** of a linear equation.

Standard Form of a Linear Equation	$Ax + By = C$, where $A \geq 0$, A and B are not both zero, and C are integers whose GCF is 1.

Example 1 Determine whether $y = 6 - 3x$ is a linear equation. If so, write the equation in standard form.

First rewrite the equation so both variables are on the same side of the equation.

$y = 6 - 3x$ Original equation
$y + 3x = 6 - 3x + 3x$ Add $3x$ to each side.
$3x + y = 6$ Simplify.

The equation is now in standard form, with $A = 3$, $B = 1$ and $C = 6$. This is a linear equation.

Example 2 Determine whether $3xy + y = 4 + 2x$ is a linear equation. If so, write the equation in standard form.

Since the term $3xy$ has two variables, the equation cannot be written in the form $Ax + By = C$. Therefore, this is not a linear equation.

Exercises

Determine whether each equation is a linear equation. If so, write the equation in standard form.

1. $2x = 4y$
yes; $2x - 4y = 0$

2. $6 + y = 8$
yes; $y = 2$

3. $4x - 2y = -1$
yes; $4x - 2y = -1$

4. $3xy + 8 = 4y$
no

5. $3x - 4 = 12$
yes; $3x = 16$

6. $y = x^2 + 7$
no

7. $y - 4x = 9$
yes; $4x - y = -9$

8. $x + 8 = 0$
yes; $x = -8$

9. $-2x + 3 = 4y$
yes; $2x + 4y = 3$

10. $2 + \frac{1}{2}x = y$
yes; $x - 2y = -4$

11. $\frac{1}{4}y = 12 - 4x$
yes; $16x + y = 48$

12. $3xy - y = 8$
no

13. $6x + 4y - 3 = 0$
yes; $6x + 4y = 3$

14. $yx - 2 = 8$
no

15. $6a - 2b = 8 + b$
yes; $6a - 3b = 8$

16. $\frac{1}{4}x - 12y = 1$
yes; $x - 48y = 4$

17. $3 + x + x^2 = 0$
no

18. $x^2 = 2xy$
no

© Glencoe/McGraw-Hill   237   *Glencoe Algebra 1*

Lesson 4-5

NAME _____ DATE _____ PERIOD _____

4-5 Study Guide and Intervention *(continued)*
Graphing Linear Equations

Graph Linear Equations The graph of a linear equation is a line. The line represents all solutions to the linear equation. Also, every ordered pair on this line satisfies the equation.

Example Graph the equation $y - 2x = 1$.

Solve the equation for y.

$y - 2x = 1$ Original equation
$y - 2x + 2x = 1 + 2x$ Add $2x$ to each side.
$y = 2x + 1$ Simplify.

Select five values for the domain and make a table. Then graph the ordered pairs and draw a line through the points.

x	$2x + 1$	y	(x, y)
-2	$2(-2) + 1$	-3	$(-2, -3)$
-1	$2(-1) + 1$	-1	$(-1, -1)$
0	$2(0) + 1$	1	$(0, 1)$
1	$2(1) + 1$	3	$(1, 3)$
2	$2(2) + 1$	5	$(2, 5)$

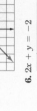

Exercises

Graph each equation.

1. $y = 4$

2. $y = 2x$
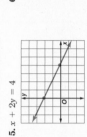

3. $x - y = -1$

4. $3x + 2y = 6$

5. $x + 2y = 4$
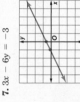

6. $2x + y = -2$

7. $3x - 6y = -3$
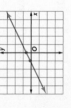

8. $-2x + y = -2$

9. $\frac{1}{4}x + \frac{3}{4}y = 6$

© Glencoe/McGraw-Hill   238   *Glencoe Algebra 1*

Skills Practice 4-5
Graphing Linear Equations

NAME _____ DATE _____ PERIOD _____

Determine whether each equation is a linear equation. If so, write the equation in standard form.

1. $xy = 6$
no

2. $y = 2 - 3x$
yes; $3x + y = 2$

3. $5x = y - 4$
yes; $5x - y = -4$

4. $y = 2x + 5$
yes; $2x - y = -5$

5. $y = -7 + 6x$
yes; $6x - y = 7$

6. $y = 3x^2 + 1$
no

7. $y - 4 = 0$
yes; $y = 4$

8. $5x + 6y = 3x + 2$
yes; $x + 3y = 1$

9. $\frac{1}{2}y = 1$
yes; $y = 2$

Graph each equation.

10. $y = 4$
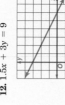

11. $y = 3x$

12. $y = x + 4$

13. $y = x - 2$

14. $y = 4 - x$

15. $y = 4 - 2x$

16. $x - y = 3$

17. $10x = -5y$

18. $4x = 2y + 6$

239 *Glencoe Algebra 1*

Practice (Average) 4-5
Graphing Linear Equations

NAME _____ DATE _____ PERIOD _____

Determine whether each equation is a linear equation. If so, write the equation in standard form.

1. $4xy + 2y = 9$
no

2. $8x - 3y = 6 - 4x$
yes; $4x - y = 2$

3. $7x + y + 3 = y$
yes; $7x = -3$

4. $5 - 2y = 3x$
yes; $3x + 2y = 5$

5. $4y + x = 9x$
yes; $8x - 4y = 0$

6. $a + \frac{1}{5}b = 2$
yes; $5a + b = 10$

7. $6x = 2y$
yes; $6x - 2y = 0$

8. $\frac{x}{4} - \frac{y}{3} = 1$
yes; $3x - 4y = 12$

9. $\frac{5}{x} - \frac{2}{y} = 7$
no

Graph each equation.

10. $\frac{1}{2}x - y = 2$

11. $5x - 2y = 7$
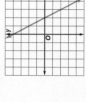

12. $1.5x + 3y = 9$

COMMUNICATIONS For Exercises 13–15, use the following information.

A telephone company charges $4.95 per month for long distance calls plus $0.05 per minute. The monthly cost c of long distance calls can be described by the equation $c = 0.05m + 4.95$, where m is the number of minutes.

13. Find the y-intercept of the graph of the equation. (0, 4.95)

14. Graph the equation.
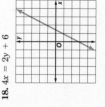
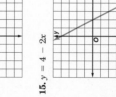

Long Distance

15. If you talk 140 minutes, what is the monthly cost for long distance? **$11.95**

MARINE BIOLOGY For Exercises 16 and 17, use the following information.

Killer whales usually swim at a rate of 3.2–9.7 kilometers per hour, though they can travel up to 48.4 kilometers per hour. Suppose a migrating killer whale is swimming at an average rate of 4.5 kilometers per hour. The distance d the whale has traveled in t hours can be predicted by the equation $d = 4.5t$.

16. Graph the equation.
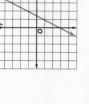
Killer Whale Travels

17. Use the graph to predict the time it takes the killer whale to travel 30 kilometers. **between 6 h and 7 h**

240 *Glencoe Algebra 1*

Lesson 4-5

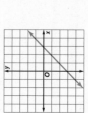
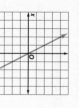
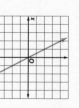

Answers

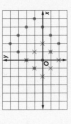

4-5 Enrichment

Taxicab Graphs

You have used a rectangular coordinate system to graph equations such as $y = x - 1$ on a coordinate plane. In a coordinate plane, the numbers in an ordered pair (x, y) can be any two real numbers.

A **taxicab plane** is different from the usual coordinate plane. The only points allowed are those that exist along the horizontal and vertical grid lines. You may think of the points as taxicabs that must stay on the streets.

The taxicab graph shows the equations $y = -2$ and $y = x - 1$. Notice that one of the graphs is no longer a straight line. It is now a collection of separate points.

Graph these equations on the taxicab plane at the right.

1. $y = x + 1$ **2.** $y = -2x + 3$

3. $y = 2.5$ **4.** $x = -4$

Use your graphs for these problems.

5. Which of the equations has the same graph in both the usual coordinate plane and the taxicab plane? $x = -4$

6. Describe the form of equations that have the same graph in both the usual coordinate plane and the taxicab plane.
$x = A$ and $y = B$, where A and B are integers

In the taxicab plane, distances are not measured diagonally, but along the streets. Write the taxi-distance between each pair of points.

7. (0, 0) and (5, 2)   **8.** (0, 0) and (-3, 2)   **9.** (0, 0) and (2, 1.5)
7 units   5 units   3.5 units

10. (1, 2) and (4, 3)   **11.** (2, 4) and (-1, 3)   **12.** (0, 4) and (-2, 0)
4 units   4 units   6 units

Draw these graphs on the taxicab grid at the right.

13. The set of points whose taxi-distance from (0, 0) is 2 units. indicated by crosses

14. The set of points whose taxi-distance from (2, 1) is 3 units. indicated by dots

242   *Glencoe Algebra 1*

4-5 Reading to Learn Mathematics

Graphing Linear Equations

Pre-Activity   How can linear equations be used in nutrition?

Read the introduction to Lesson 4-5 at the top of page 218 in your textbook.
In the equation $f = 0.3\left(\dfrac{C}{9}\right)$, what are the independent and dependent variables? C is independent, f is dependent.

Reading the Lesson

1. Describe the graph of a linear equation. The graph is a straight line.

2. Determine whether each equation is a linear equation. Explain.

	Equation	Linear or non-linear?	Explanation
a.	$2x = 3y + 1$	linear	The equation can be written as $2x - 3y = 1$.
b.	$4xy + 2y = 7$	non-linear	$4xy$ has two variables.
c.	$2x^2 = 4y - 3$	non-linear	The variable x has an exponent of 2.
d.	$\dfrac{x}{5} - \dfrac{4y}{3} = 2$	linear	The equation can be written as $3x - 20y = 30$.

3. What do the terms *x-intercept* and *y-intercept* mean? The *x*-intercept is the *x*-coordinate of the point where the graph of an equation crosses the *x*-axis, and the *y*-intercept is the *y*-coordinate of the point where the graph crosses the *y*-axis.

Helping You Remember

4. Describe the method you would use to graph $4x + 2y = 8$. Sample answer: Find the *x*- and *y*-intercepts, which are 2 and 4. Plot the points for the ordered pairs (2, 0) and (0, 4), and draw a line that connects the points.

241   *Glencoe Algebra 1*

NAME _____ DATE _____ PERIOD _____

4-6 Study Guide and Intervention

Functions

Identify Functions Relations in which each element of the domain is paired with exactly one element of the range are called **functions**.

Example 1 Determine whether the relation {(6, −3), (4, 1), (7, −2), (−3, 1)} is a function. Explain.

Since each element of the domain is paired with exactly one element of the range, this relation is a function.

Example 2 Determine whether $3x - y = 6$ is a function.

Since the equation is in the form $Ax + By = C$, the graph of the equation will be a line, as shown at the right.

If you draw a vertical line through each value of x, the vertical line passes through just one point of the graph. Thus, the line represents a function.

Exercises

Determine whether each relation is a function.

1.
yes

2.
yes

3.
no

4.
no

5.
no

6.
yes

7. {(4, 2), (2, 3), (6, 1)}
yes

8. {(−3, −3), (−3, 4), (−2, 4)}
no

9. {(−1, 0), (1, 0)}
yes

10. $-2x + 4y = 0$
yes

11. $x^2 + y^2 = 8$
no

12. $x = -4$
no

NAME _____ DATE _____ PERIOD _____

4-6 Study Guide and Intervention *(continued)*

Functions

Function Values Equations that are functions can be written in a form called **function notation**. For example, $y = 2x - 1$ can be written as $f(x) = 2x - 1$. In the function, x represents the elements of the domain, and $f(x)$ represents the elements of the range. Suppose you want to find the value in the range that corresponds to the element 2 in the domain. This is written $f(2)$ and is read "f of 2." The value of $f(2)$ is found by substituting 2 for x in the equation.

Example If $f(x) = 3x - 4$, find each value.

a. $f(3)$

$f(3) = 3(3) - 4$ Replace x with 3.
$= 9 - 4$ Multiply.
$= 5$ Simplify.

b. $f(-2)$

$f(-2) = 3(-2) - 4$ Replace x with −2.
$= -6 - 4$ Multiply.
$= -10$ Simplify.

Exercises

If $f(x) = 2x - 4$ and $g(x) = x^2 - 4x$, find each value.

1. $f(4)$
4

2. $g(2)$
−4

3. $f(-5)$
−14

4. $g(-3)$
21

5. $f(0)$
−4

6. $g(0)$
0

7. $f(3) - 1$
1

8. $f\left(\dfrac{1}{4}\right)$
$-3\dfrac{1}{2}$

9. $g\left(\dfrac{1}{4}\right)$
$-\dfrac{15}{16}$

10. $f(a^2)$
$2a^2 - 4$

11. $f(k + 1)$
$2k - 2$

12. $g(2c)$
$4c^2 - 8c$

13. $f(3x)$
$6x - 4$

14. $f(2) + 3$
3

15. $g(-4)$
32

Skills Practice 4-6

4-6 Skills Practice
Functions

Determine whether each relation is a function.

1.

yes

2.

yes

3.

no

4.

x	y
4	−5
−1	−10
0	−9
1	−7
9	1

yes

5.

x	y
2	7
5	−3
3	5
−4	−2
5	2

no

6.

x	y
3	7
−1	1
1	0
3	5
7	3

no

7. {(2, 5), (4, −2), (3, 3), (5, 4), (−2, 5)} **yes**   8. {(6, −1), (−4, 2), (5, 2), (4, 6), (6, 5)} **no**

9. $y = 2x − 5$ **yes**   10. $y = 11$ **yes**

11.

yes

12.

no

13.

no

If $f(x) = 3x + 2$ and $g(x) = x^2 − x$, find each value.

14. $f(4)$ **14**   15. $f(8)$ **26**

16. $f(−2)$ **−4**   17. $g(2)$ **2**

18. $g(−3)$ **12**   19. $g(−6)$ **42**

20. $f(2) + 1$ **9**   21. $f(1) − 1$ **4**

22. $g(2) − 2$ **0**   23. $g(−1) + 4$ **6**

24. $f(x + 1)$ **$3x + 5$**   25. $g(3b)$ **$9b^2 − 3b$**

Practice 4-6

4-6 Practice (Average)
Functions

Determine whether each relation is a function.

1.

yes

2.

x	y
1	−5
−4	3
7	6
1	−2

no

3.

yes

4. {(1, 4), (2, −2), (3, −6), (−6, 3), (−3, 6)} **yes**   5. {(6, −4), (2, −4), (−4, 2), (4, 6), (2, 6)} **no**

6. $x = −2$ **no**   7. $y = 2$ **yes**

If $f(x) = 2x − 6$ and $g(x) = x − 2x^2$, find each value.

8. $f(2)$ **−2**   9. $f\left(−\dfrac{1}{2}\right)$ **−7**

11. $g\left(−\dfrac{1}{3}\right)$ **$−\dfrac{5}{9}$**   12. $f(7)$ **9**   −1   10. $g(−1)$ **−3**

14. $f(h + 9)$ **$2h + 12$**   15. $g(3y)$ **$3y − 18y^2$**   13. $g(−3) + 13$ **−8**

16. $2[g(b) + 1]$ **$2b − 4b^2 + 2$**

WAGES For Exercises 17 and 18, use the following information.

Martin earns $7.50 per hour proofreading ads at a local newspaper. His weekly wage w can be described by the equation $w = 7.5h$, where h is the number of hours worked.

17. Write the equation in functional notation. **$f(h) = 7.5h$**

18. Find $f(15)$, $f(20)$, and $f(25)$. **112.50, 150, 187.50**

ELECTRICITY For Exercises 19–21, use the following information.

The table shows the relationship between resistance R and current I in a circuit.

Resistance (ohms)	120	80	48	6	4
Current (amperes)	0.1	0.15	0.25	2	3

19. Is the relationship a function? Explain. **Yes; for each value in the domain, there is only one value in the range.**

20. If the relation can be represented by the equation $IR = 12$, rewrite the equation in functional notation so that the resistance R is a function of the current I. **$f(I) = \dfrac{12}{I}$**

21. What is the resistance in a circuit when the current is 0.5 ampere? **24 ohms**

Lesson 4-6

4-6 Reading to Learn Mathematics

Functions

Pre-Activity How are functions used in meteorology?

Read the introduction to Lesson 4-6 at the top of page 226 in your textbook.

If pressure is the independent variable and temperature is the dependent variable, what are the ordered pairs for this set of data?

{(1013, 3), (1006, 4), (997, 10), (995, 13), (995, 8), (1000, 4), (1006, 1), (1011, −2), (1016, −6), (1019, −9)}

Reading the Lesson

1. The statement, "Relations in which each element of the domain are paired with exactly one element of the range is called functions," is false. How can you change the underlined words to make the statement true? **Change *range* to *domain* and *domain* to *range*.**

2. Describe how each method shows that the relation represented is a function.

   a. mapping

   The elements of the domain are paired with corresponding elements in the range. Each element of the domain has only one arrow going from it.

   b. vertical line test

   No vertical line passes through more than one point of the graph.

Helping You Remember

3. A student who was trying to help a friend remember how functions are different from relations that are not functions gave the following advice: *Just remember that functions are very strict and never give you a choice.* Explain how this might help you remember what a function is. **Sample answer: A function always pairs each element in the domain with exactly one element in the range. If two people start with the same element of the domain, they are forced to pair it with the same element in the range. The second person cannot pick a different number from the first person.**

4-6 Enrichment

Composite Functions

Three things are needed to have a function—a set called the domain, a set called the range, and a rule that matches each element in the domain with only one element in the range. Here is an example.

Rule: $f(x) = 2x + 1$

$f(x) = 2x + 1$

$f(1) = 2(1) + 1 = 2 + 1 = 3$

$f(2) = 2(2) + 1 = 4 + 1 = 5$

$f(-3) = 2(-3) + 1 = -6 + 1 = -5$

Suppose we have three sets A, B, and C and two functions described as shown below.

Rule: $f(x) = 2x + 1$ Rule: $g(y) = 3y - 4$

$g(y) = 3y - 4$

$g(3) = 3(3) - 4 = 5$

Let's find a rule that will match elements of set A with elements of set C without finding any elements in set B. In other words, let's find a rule for the **composite function** $g[f(x)]$.

Since $f(x) = 2x + 1$, $g[f(x)] = g(2x + 1)$.

Since $g(y) = 3y - 4$, $g(2x + 1) = 3(2x + 1) - 4$, or $6x - 1$.

Therefore, $g[f(x)] = 6x - 1$.

Find a rule for the composite function $g[f(x)]$.

1. $f(x) = 3x$ and $g(y) = 2y + 1$

   $g[f(x)] = 6x + 1$

2. $f(x) = x^2 + 1$ and $g(y) = 4y$

   $g[f(x)] = 4x^2 + 4$

3. $f(x) = -2x$ and $g(y) = y^2 - 3y$

   $g[f(x)] = 4x^2 + 6x$

4. $f(x) = \dfrac{1}{x-3}$ and $g(y) = y^{-1}$

   $g[f(x)] = x - 3$

5. Is it always the case that $g[f(x)] = f[g(x)]$? Justify your answer.
   No. For example, in Exercise 1,
   $f[g(x)] = f(2x + 1) = 3(2x + 1) = 6x + 3$, not $6x + 1$.

Answers

Page 249 (left)

4-7 Study Guide and Intervention

Arithmetic Sequences

Recognize Arithmetic Sequences A **sequence** is a set of numbers in a specific order. If the difference between successive terms is constant, then the sequence is called an **arithmetic sequence**.

Arithmetic Sequence	a numerical pattern that increases or decreases at a constant rate or value called the **common difference**

Example 1 Determine whether the sequence 1, 3, 5, 7, 9, 11, … is an arithmetic sequence. Justify your answer.

If possible, find the common difference between the terms. Since $3 - 1 = 2$, $5 - 3 = 2$, and so on, the common difference is 2.

Since the difference between the terms of 1, 3, 5, 7, 9, 11, … is constant, this is an arithmetic sequence.

Example 2 Determine whether the sequence 1, 2, 4, 8, 16, 32, … is an arithmetic sequence. Justify your answer.

If possible, find the common difference between the terms. Since $2 - 1 = 1$ and $4 - 2 = 2$, there is no common difference.

Since the difference between the terms of 1, 2, 4, 8, 16, 32, … is not constant, this is not an arithmetic sequence.

Exercises

Determine whether each sequence is an arithmetic sequence. If it is, state the common difference.

1. 1, 5, 9, 13, 17, …
yes; 4

2. 8, 4, 0, −4, −8, …
yes; −4

3. 1, 3, 9, 27, 81, …
no

4. 10, 15, 25, 40, 60, …
no

5. −10, −5, 0, 5, 10, …
yes; 5

6. 8, 6, 4, 2, 0, −2, …
yes; −2

7. 4, 8, 12, 16, …
yes; 4

8. 15, 12, 10, 9, …
no

9. 1.1, 2.1, 3.1, 4.1, 5.1, …
yes; 1

10. 8, 7, 6, 5, 4, …
yes; −1

11. 0.5, 1.5, 2.5, 3.5, 4.5, …
yes; 1

12. 1, 4, 16, 64, …
no

13. 10, 14, 18, 22, …
yes; 4

14. −3, −6, −9, −12, …
yes; −3

15. 7, 0, −7, −14, …
yes; −7

Page 250 (right)

4-7 Study Guide and Intervention *(continued)*

Arithmetic Sequences

Write Arithmetic Sequences You can use the common difference of an arithmetic sequence to find the next term of the sequence. Each term after the first term is found by adding the preceding term and the common difference.

Terms of an Arithmetic Sequence	If a_1 is the first term of an arithmetic sequence with common difference d, then the sequence is a_1, $a_1 + d$, $a_1 + 2d$, $a_1 + 3d$, ….
nth Term of an Arithmetic Sequence	$a_n = a_1 + (n - 1)d$

Example 1 Find the next three terms of the arithmetic sequence 28, 32, 36, 40, ….

Find the common difference by subtracting successive terms.

28   32   36   40
  +4   +4   +4

The common difference is 4.
Add 4 to the last given term, 40, to get the next term. Continue adding 4 until the next three terms are found.

40   44   48   52
  +4   +4   +4

The next three terms are 44, 48, 52.

Example 2 Write an equation for the nth term of the sequence 12, 15, 18, 21, … .

In this sequence, a_1 is 12. Find the common difference.

12   15   18   21
  +3   +3   +3

The common difference is 3.
Use the formula for the nth term to write an equation.

$a_n = a_1 + (n - 1)d$ Formula for the nth term
$a_n = 12 + (n - 1)3$ $a_1 = 12$, $d = 3$
$a_n = 12 + 3n - 3$ Distributive Property
$a_n = 3n + 9$ Simplify.

The equation for the nth term is $a_n = 3n + 9$.

Exercises

Find the next three terms of each arithmetic sequence.

1. 9, 13, 17, 21, 25, …
29, 33, 37

2. 4, 0, −4, −8, −12, …
−16, −20, −24

3. 29, 35, 41, 47, …
53, 59, 65

4. −10, −5, 0, 5, …
10, 15, 20

5. 2.5, 5, 7.5, 10, …
12.5, 15, 17.5

6. 3.1, 4.1, 5.1, 6.1, …
7.1, 8.1, 9.1

Find the nth term of each arithmetic sequence described.

7. $a_1 = 6$, $d = 3$, $n = 10$
33

8. $a_1 = -2$, $d = -3$, $n = 8$
−23

9. $a_1 = 1$, $d = -5$, $n = 20$
−94

10. $a_1 = -3$, $d = -2$, $n = 50$
−101

11. $a_1 = -12$, $d = 4$, $n = 20$
64

12. $a_1 = 1$, $d = \frac{1}{2}$, $n = 11$
6

Write an equation for the nth term of the arithmetic sequence.

13. 1, 3, 5, 7, …
$a_n = 2n - 1$

14. −1, −4, −7, −10, …
$a_n = -3n + 2$

15. −4, −9, −14, −19, …
$a_n = -5n + 1$

4-7 Skills Practice

Arithmetic Sequences

NAME _____ DATE _____ PERIOD _____

Determine whether each sequence is an arithmetic sequence. If it is, state the common difference.

1. $4, 7, 9, 12, \ldots$ **no**

2. $15, 13, 11, 9, \ldots$ **yes; -2**

3. $7, 10, 13, 16, \ldots$ **yes; 3**

4. $-6, -5, -3, -1, \ldots$ **no**

5. $-5, -3, -1, 1, \ldots$ **yes; 2**

6. $-9, -12, -15, -18, \ldots$ **yes; -3**

Find the next three terms of each arithmetic sequence.

7. $3, 7, 11, 15, \ldots$ **19, 23, 27**

8. $22, 20, 18, 16, \ldots$ **14, 12, 10**

9. $-13, -11, -9, -7, \ldots$ **$-5, -3, -1$**

10. $-2, -5, -8, -11, \ldots$ **$-14, -17, -20$**

11. $19, 24, 29, 34, \ldots$ **39, 44, 49**

12. $16, 7, -2, -11, \ldots$ **$-20, -29, -38$**

Find the nth term of each arithmetic sequence described.

13. $a_1 = 6, d = 3, n = 12$ **39**

14. $a_1 = -2, d = 5, n = 11$ **48**

15. $a_1 = 10, d = -3, n = 15$ **-32**

16. $a_1 = -3, d = -3, n = 22$ **-66**

17. $a_1 = 24, d = 8, n = 25$ **216**

18. $a_1 = 8, d = -6, n = 14$ **-70**

19. $8, 13, 18, 23, \ldots$ for $n = 17$ **88**

20. $-10, -3, 4, 11, \ldots$ for $n = 12$ **67**

21. $12, 10, 8, 6, \ldots$ for $n = 16$ **-18**

22. $12, 7, 2, -3, \ldots$ for $n = 25$ **-108**

Write an equation for the nth term of each arithmetic sequence. Then graph the first five terms of the sequence.

23. $7, 13, 19, 25, \ldots$
$a_n = 6n + 1$

24. $30, 26, 22, 18, \ldots$
$a_n = -4n + 34$

25. $-7, -4, -1, 2, \ldots$
$a_n = 3n - 10$

251

© Glencoe/McGraw-Hill

4-7 Practice (Average)

Arithmetic Sequences

NAME _____ DATE _____ PERIOD _____

Determine whether each sequence is an arithmetic sequence. If it is, state the common difference.

1. $21, 13, 5, -3, \ldots$ **yes; -8**

2. $-5, 12, 29, 46, \ldots$ **yes; 17**

3. $-2.2, -1.1, 0.1, 1.3, \ldots$ **no**

Find the next three terms of each arithmetic sequence.

4. $82, 76, 70, 64, \ldots$ **58, 52, 46**

5. $-49, -35, -21, -7, \ldots$ **7, 21, 35**

6. $\frac{3}{4}, \frac{1}{4}, 0, \ldots$ **$-\frac{1}{4}, -\frac{1}{2}, -\frac{3}{4}$**

Find the nth term of each arithmetic sequence described.

7. $a_1 = 7, d = 9, n = 18$ **160**

8. $a_1 = -12, d = 4, n = 36$ **128**

9. $-18, -13, -8, -3, \ldots$ for $n = 27$ **112**

10. $4.1, 4.8, 5.5, 6.2, \ldots$ for $n = 14$ **13.2**

11. $a_1 = \frac{3}{8}, d = \frac{1}{4}, n = 15$ **$3\frac{7}{8}$**

12. $a_1 = 2\frac{1}{2}, d = 1\frac{1}{2}, n = 24$ **37**

Write an equation for the nth term of each arithmetic sequence. Then graph the first five terms of the sequence.

13. $9, 13, 17, 21, \ldots$
$a_n = 4n + 5$

14. $-5, -2, 1, 4, \ldots$
$a_n = 3n - 8$

15. $19, 31, 43, 55, \ldots$
$a_n = 12n + 7$

BANKING For Exercises 16 and 17, use the following information.
Chem deposited $115.00 in a savings account. Each week thereafter, he deposits $35.00 into the account.

16. Write a formula to find the total amount Chem has deposited for any particular number of weeks after his initial deposit. $a_n = 35n + 115$

17. How much has Chem deposited 30 weeks after his initial deposit? **$1165**

18. STORE DISPLAY Tamika is stacking boxes of tissue for a store display. Each row of tissues has 2 fewer boxes than the row below. The first row has 23 boxes of tissues. How many boxes will there be in the tenth row? **5**

252

© Glencoe/McGraw-Hill

Page 253

Lesson 4-7

4-7 Reading to Learn Mathematics
Arithmetic Sequences

Pre-Activity **How are arithmetic sequences used to solve problems in science?**

Read the introduction to Lesson 4-7 at the top of page 233 in your textbook.
Describe the pattern in the data. **The altitude of the probe increases by 8.2 feet each second.**

Reading the Lesson

1. Do the recorded altitudes in the introduction form an arithmetic sequence? Explain.
Yes; the difference between the successive terms is the constant 8.2.

2. What is meant by *successive terms*? **terms that come one right after the other**

3. Complete the table.

Pattern	Is the sequence increasing or decreasing?	Is there a common difference? If so, what is it?
a. 2, 5, 8, 11, 14, …	increasing	yes; 3
b. 55, 50, 45, 40, …	decreasing	yes; −5
c. 1, 2, 4, 9, 16, …	increasing	no
d. $\frac{1}{2}$, 0, $-\frac{1}{2}$, −1, …	decreasing	yes; $-\frac{1}{2}$
e. 2.6, 2.9, 3.2, 3.5, …	increasing	yes; 0.3

Helping You Remember

4. Use the pattern 3, 7, 11, 15, … to explain how you would help someone else learn how to find the 10th term of an arithmetic sequence. Find the common difference of 4. **To find the 10th term, use the formula $a_n = a_1 + (n - 1)d$. Substitute 10 for n, 3 for a_1, and 4 for d. The 10th term is 39.**

Page 254

4-7 Enrichment

Arithmetic Series

An arithmetic series is a series in which each term after the first may be found by adding the same number to the preceding term. Let S stand for the following series in which each term is 3 more than the preceding one.

$$S = 2 + 5 + 8 + 11 + 14 + 17 + 20$$

The series remains the same if we reverse the order of all the terms. So let us reverse the order of the terms and add one series to the other, term by term. This is shown at the right.

$$\begin{aligned} S &= 2 + 5 + 8 + 11 + 14 + 17 + 20 \\ S &= 20 + 17 + 14 + 11 + 8 + 5 + 2 \\ \hline 2S &= 22 + 22 + 22 + 22 + 22 + 22 + 22 \\ 2S &= 7(22) \\ S &= \frac{7(22)}{2} = 7(11) = 77 \end{aligned}$$

Let a represent the first term of the series.
Let ℓ represent the last term of the series.
Let n represent the number of terms in the series.

In the preceding example, $a = 2$, $\ell = 20$, and $n = 7$. Notice that when you add the two series, term by term, the sum of each pair of terms is 22. That sum can be found by adding the first and last terms, $2 + 20$ or $a + \ell$. Notice also that there are 7, or n, such sums. Therefore, the value of $2S$ is $7(22)$, or $n(a + \ell)$ in the general case. Since this is twice the sum of the series, you can use the following formula to find the sum of any arithmetic series.

$$S = \frac{n(a + \ell)}{2}$$

Example 1 **Find the sum: $1 + 2 + 3 + 4 + 5 + 6 + 7 + 8 + 9$**

$a = 1$, $\ell = 9$, $n = 9$, so $S = \dfrac{9(1 + 9)}{2} = \dfrac{9 \cdot 10}{2} = 45$

Example 2 **Find the sum: $-9 + (-5) + (-1) + 3 + 7 + 11 + 15$**

$a = 29$, $\ell = 15$, $n = 7$, so $S = \dfrac{7(-9 + 15)}{2} = \dfrac{7 \cdot 6}{2} = 21$

Find the sum of each arithmetic series.

1. $3 + 6 + 9 + 12 + 15 + 18 + 21 + 24$ **108**

2. $10 + 15 + 20 + 25 + 30 + 35 + 40 + 45 + 50$ **270**

3. $-21 + (-16) + (-11) + (-6) + (-1) + 4 + 9 + 14$ **−28**

4. even whole numbers from 2 through 100   **2550**

5. odd whole numbers between 0 and 100   **2500**

4-8 Study Guide and Intervention
Writing Equations from Patterns

Look for Patterns A very common problem-solving strategy is to **look for a pattern.** Arithmetic sequences follow a pattern, and other sequences can follow a pattern.

Example 1 Find the next three terms in the sequence 3, 9, 27, 81, ….

Study the pattern in the sequence.

3   9   27   81
  ×3   ×3   ×3

Successive terms are found by multiplying the last given term by 3.

81   243   729   2187
   ×3   ×3   ×3

The next three terms are 243, 729, 2187.

Example 2 Find the next three terms in the sequence 10, 6, 11, 7, 12, 8, ….

Study the pattern in the sequence.

10   6   11   7   12   8
   −4   +5   −4   +5   −4

Assume that the pattern continues.

8   13   9   14
  +5   −4   +5

The next three terms are 13, 9, 14.

Exercises

1. Give the next two items for the pattern below.

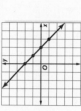

Give the next three numbers in each sequence.

2. 2, 12, 72, 432, …
2592, 15,552, 93,312

3. 7, −14, 28, −56, …
112, −224, 448

4. 0, 0, 10, 5, 15, 10, …
20, 15, 25

5. 0, 0, 1, 3, 6, 10, …
15, 21, 28

6. $x − 1, x − 2, x − 3, …$
$x − 4, x − 5, x − 6$

7. $x, \dfrac{x}{2}, \dfrac{x}{3}, \dfrac{x}{4}, …$
$\dfrac{x}{5}, \dfrac{x}{6}, \dfrac{x}{7}$

4-8 Study Guide and Intervention (continued)
Writing Equations from Patterns

Write Equations Sometimes a pattern can lead to a general rule that can be written as an equation.

Example Suppose you purchased a number of packages of blank compact disks. If each package contains 3 compact disks, you could make a chart to show the relationship between the number of packages of compact disks and the number of disks purchased. Use x for the number of packages and y for the number of compact disks.

Make a table of ordered pairs for several points of the graph.

Number of Packages	1	2	3	4	5
Number of CDs	3	6	9	12	15

The difference in the x values is 1, and the difference in the y values is 3. This pattern shows that y is always three times x. This suggests the relation $y = 3x$. Since the relation is also a function, we can write the equation in functional notation as $f(x) = 3x$.

Exercises

1. Write an equation for the function in functional notation. Then complete the table.

x	−1	0	1	2	3	4
y	−2	2	6	10	14	18

$f(x) = 4x + 2$

2. Write an equation for the function in functional notation. Then complete the table.

x	−2	−1	0	1	2	3
y	10	7	4	1	−2	−5

$f(x) = −3x + 4$

3. Write an equation in functional notation.

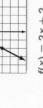

$f(x) = −x + 2$

4. Write an equation in functional notation.

$f(x) = 2x + 2$

Lesson 4-8

NAME _____ DATE _____ PERIOD _____

4-8 Practice (Average)
Writing Equations from Patterns

1. Give the next two items for the pattern. Then find the 21st figure in the pattern.

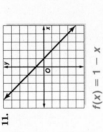

Find the next three terms in each sequence.

2. -5, -2, -3, 0, -1, 2, 1, 4, ... **3, 6, 5**

3. 0, 1, 3, 6, 10, 15, ... **21, 28, 36**

4. 0, 1, 8, 27, ... **64, 125, 216**

5. 3, 2, 4, 3, 5, 4, ... **6, 5, 7**

6. $a + 1, a + 4, a + 9, ...$ **$a + 16, a + 25, a + 36$**

7. $3d - 1, 4d - 2, 5d - 3, ...$ **$6d - 4, 7d - 5, 8d - 6$**

Write an equation in function notation for each relation.

8. 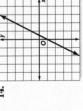 $f(x) = -\frac{1}{2}x$

9. 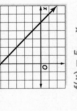 $f(x) = 3x - 6$

10. 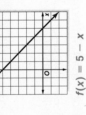 $f(x) = 2x + 4$

BIOLOGY For Exercises 11 and 12, use the following information.
Male fireflies flash in various patterns to signal location and perhaps to ward off predators. Different species of fireflies have different flash characteristics, such as the intensity of the flash, its rate, and its shape. The table below shows the rate at which a male firefly is flashing.

Time (seconds)	1	2	3	4	5
Number of Flashes	2	4	6	8	10

11. Write an equation in function notation for the relation. **$f(t) = 2t$, where t is the time in seconds and $f(t)$ is the number of flashes**

12. How many times will the firefly flash in 20 seconds? **40**

13. GEOMETRY The table shows the number of diagonals that can be drawn from one vertex in a polygon. Write an equation in function notation for the relation and find the number of diagonals that can be drawn from one vertex in a 12-sided polygon. **$f(s) = s - 3$, where s is the number of sides and $f(s)$ is the number of diagonals; 9**

Sides	3	4	5	6
Diagonals	0	1	2	3

Lesson 4-8

NAME _____ DATE _____ PERIOD _____

4-8 Skills Practice
Writing Equations from Patterns

Find the next two items for each pattern. Then find the 19th figure in the pattern.

1.

2.

Find the next three terms in each sequence.

3. 1, 4, 10, 19, 31, ... **46, 64, 85**

4. 15, 14, 16, 15, 17, 16, ... **18, 17, 19**

5. 29, 28, 26, 23, 19, ... **14, 8, 1**

6. 2, 3, 2, 4, 2, 5, ... **2, 6, 2**

7. $x, x - 1, x - 2, ...$ **$x - 3, x - 4, x - 5$**

8. $y, 4y, 9y, 16y, ...$ **$25y, 36y, 49y$**

Write an equation in function notation for each relation.

9.  $f(x) = -2x$

10. $f(x) = x - 2$

11. $f(x) = 1 - x$

12. $f(x) = x + 6$

13. $f(x) = 5 - x$

14. $f(x) = 2x - 1$

Page 259 — Reading to Learn Mathematics

NAME _____ DATE _____ PERIOD _____

4-8 Reading to Learn Mathematics

Writing Equations From Patterns

Pre-Activity **Why is writing equations from patterns important in science?**

Read the introduction to Lesson 4-8 at the top of page 240 in your textbook.

- What is meant by the term *linear pattern*? The points line up along a straight line.

- Describe any arithmetic sequences in the data. Both the volume of water and the volume of ice are arithmetic sequences. The volume of water has a common difference of 11 and the volume of ice has a common difference of 12.

Reading the Lesson

1. What is meant by the term *inductive reasoning*? making a conclusion based on a pattern of examples

2. For the figures below, explain why Figure 5 does not follow the pattern.

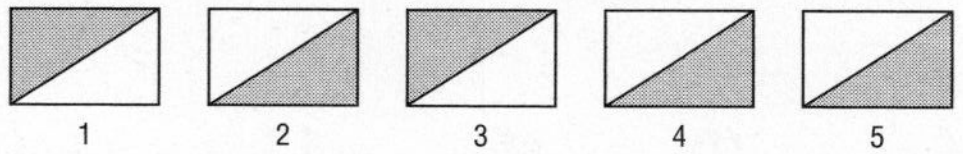

If you follow the pattern of shading the top triangle, then the bottom, then the top, and so on, Figure 5 should have the top triangle shaded.

3. Describe the steps you would use to find the pattern in the sequence 1, 5, 25, 125, … . Subtract successive terms to find out if it is an arithmetic sequence. It is not. So study the successive terms to see if multiplication or division is used. The pattern is to multiply each term by 5 to get the next term.

Helping You Remember

4. What are some basic things to remember when you are trying to discover whether there is a pattern in a sequence of numbers? Sample answer: Look to see whether successive terms increase or decrease by the same amount. If not, look to see whether successive terms have been multiplied or divided by the same number.

Page 260 — Enrichment

NAME _____ DATE _____ PERIOD _____

4-8 Enrichment

Traceable Figures

Try to trace over each of the figures below without tracing the same segment twice.

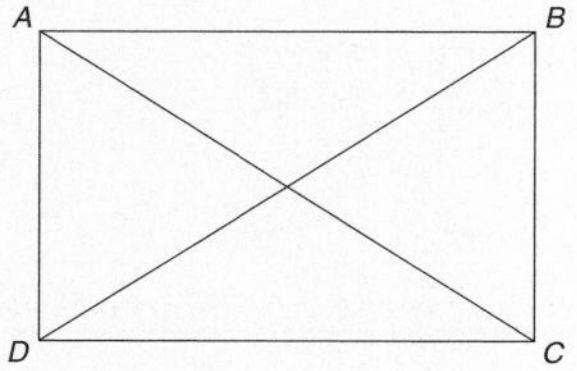

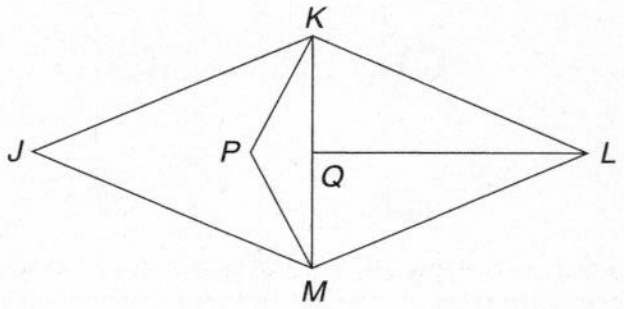

The figure at the left cannot be traced, but the one at the right can. The rule is that a figure is traceable if it has no points, or exactly two points where an odd number of segments meet. The figure at the left has three segments meeting at each of the four corners. However, the figure at the right has exactly two points, *L* and *Q*, where an odd number of segments meet.

Determine whether each figure can be traced. If it can, then name the starting point and number the sides in the order in which they should be traced.

1. Yes; *E*

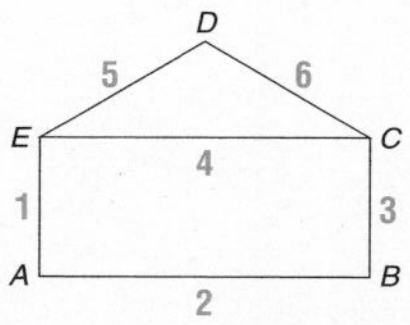

2. No

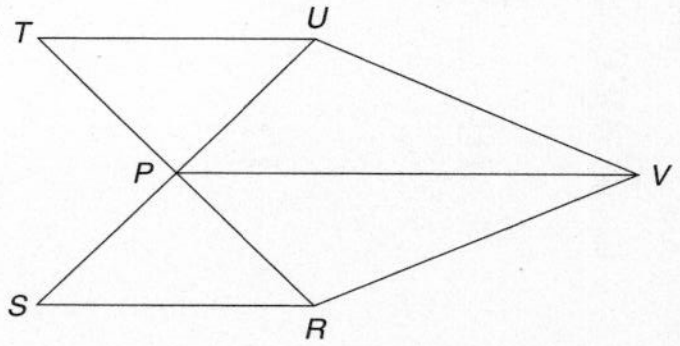

3. Yes; *X*

4. Yes; *D*

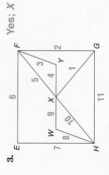

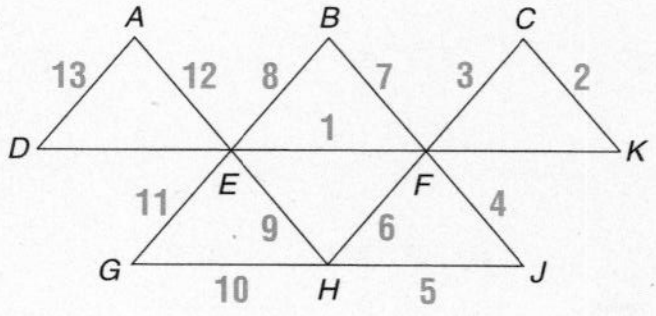

Lesson 4-8

Chapter 4 Assessment Answer Key

Form 1
Page 261

1. __C__

2. __A__

3. __D__

4. __B__

5. __A__

6. __B__

7. __C__

8. __D__

9. __B__

Page 262

10. __A__

11. __B__

12. __A__

13. __C__

14. __C__

15. __C__

16. __C__

17. __B__

18. __A__

19. __C__

20. __B__

B: __{(0, −3), (1, −2), (2, −1), (3, 0)}__

See Students' Work

Form 2A
Page 263

1. __B__

2. __D__

3. __C__

4. __C__

5. __A__

6. __C__

7. __B__

8. __C__

9. __C__

10. __D__

11. __A__

12. __C__

(continued on the next page)

Chapter 4 Assessment Answer Key

Form 2A *(continued)*
Page 264

13. D
14. C
15. B
16. B
17. D
18. A
19. A
20. B

B: {(6, 2), (4, 0), (12, −4)}

Form 2B
Page 265

1. C
2. C
3. B
4. B
5. D
6. A
7. C
8. D
9. A
10. C
11. D
12. B

Page 266

13. B
14. A
15. C
16. C
17. A
18. A
19. D
20. B

B: $-4m^2 - 10m - 6$

Answers

Chapter 4 Assessment Answer Key

Form 2C
Page 267

1. _____ (3, 1); I _____

2. _____ (−2, −3); III _____

3. _____ (2, −1); IV _____

4-6.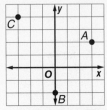

7. _____ reflection _____

8. _____ translation _____

9.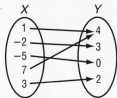

Domain:
{−5, −2, 1, 3, 7};
Range: {0, 2, 3, 4}

10. {(−3, 2), (−3, −1), (0, 1), (4, 3)}; {(2, −3), (−1, −3), (1, 0), (3, 4)}

11. {(−1, −5), (3, −3)}

12. {(−2, 5), (−1, 3), (0, 1), (1, −1), (2, −3)}

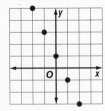

13. _____ no _____

14. yes; $2x + 3y = −4$

15.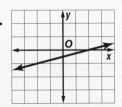

Page 268

16. _____ function _____

17. _____ not a function _____

18. _____ 8 _____

19. _____ $25v^2 + 15v − 2$ _____

20. _____ yes; 3 _____

21. _____ 36, 43, 50 _____

22. $a_n = −7n + 19$;

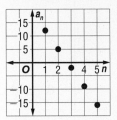

23.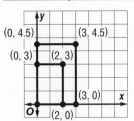

24. **Sample answer:**
$f(d) = 0.04d$

25. _____ 3 in. by 4.5 in. _____

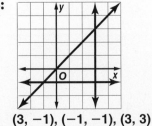

B:

(3, −1), (−1, −1), (3, 3)

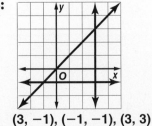

Chapter 4 Assessment Answer Key

Form 2D
Page 269

1. _____ **(2, 3); I** _____

2. _____ **(−1, 2); II** _____

3. _____ **(−2, −4); III** _____

4–6.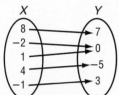

7. _____ **rotation** _____

8. _____ **dilation** _____

9.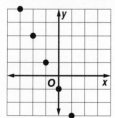

Domain:
{−2, −1, 1, 4, 8};
Range: {−5, 0, 3, 7}

10. **{(−3, 3), (−2, 0),**
(0, −1), (2, 1)}; {(3, −3),
(0, −2), (−1, 0), (1, 2)}

11. **{(−3, −16), (5, 8)}**

12. **{(−3, 5), (−2, 3),**
(−1, 1), (0, −1), (1, −3)}

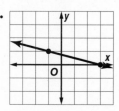

13. _____ **no** _____

14. **yes; $4x − 2y = 0$**

15.

Page 270

16. _____ **not a function** _____

17. _____ **function** _____

18. _____ **39** _____

19. _____ **$t^2 − 4t + 7$** _____

20. _____ **yes; 4** _____

21. _____ **−13, −10, −7** _____

22. **$a_n = 9n − 6$;**

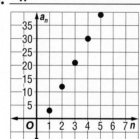

23.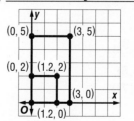

24. _____ **$f(d) = 0.05d$** _____

25. **1.2 in. by 2 in.**

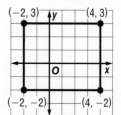

B: _____ **(−2, −2)** _____

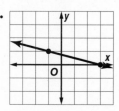

A29

Glencoe Algebra 1

Answers

Chapter 4 Assessment Answer Key

Form 3
Page 271

1. _____ **(0, −8)** _____

2.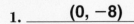
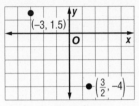

3. _____ **dilation** _____

4. **M′(1, 0), N′(−1, 2),**
   P′(−2, −3);
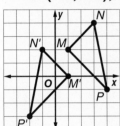

5.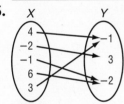

   Domain:
   {−2, −1, 3, 4, 6};
   Range: {−2, −1, 3}

6. **{(−3, 4), (−2, 1), (−1, −4),**
   (1, 1), (3, 4), (3, −3)};
   {(4, −3), (1, −2), (−4, −1),
   (1, 1), (4, 3), (−3, 3)}

7. **{(−3, −5.4), (15, 9)}**

8. **{(−4, 18), (3, −6.5),**
   (5, −13.5), (6, −17)}

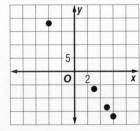

9. **yes; $3x − 7y = −6$**

Page 272

10.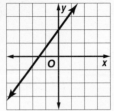

11. _____ **not a function** _____

12. _____ **function** _____

13. _____ **$−24p^2 + 16p$** _____

14. _____ **yes; $\dfrac{1}{2}$** _____

15. _____ **$y = −1$** _____

16. _____ **$a_n = 4n − 19$** _____

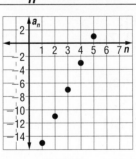

17.

18. **$V(t) = 2000 − 190t$**

19. **about $10\dfrac{1}{2}$ yrs**

20. **about 12 yrs**

B: **$\left\{(−4, −36), \left(−1, −31\dfrac{1}{2}\right),\right.$**
   $(2, −27), \left(3, −25\dfrac{1}{2}\right),$
   $(6, −21)\Big\}; \Big\{(−36, −4),$
   $\left(−31\dfrac{1}{2}, −1\right), (−27, 2),$
   $\left.\left(−25\dfrac{1}{2}, 3\right), (−21, 6)\right\}$

Glencoe Algebra 1

Chapter 4 Assessment Answer Key

Page 273, Open-Ended Assessment
Scoring Rubric

Score	General Description	Specific Criteria
4	**Superior** A correct solution that is supported by well-developed, accurate explanations	• Shows thorough understanding of the concepts of *points on the coordinate plane, transformations, relations, functions, linear equations, arithmetic sequences,* and *patterns.* • Uses appropriate strategies to solve problems. • Computations are correct. • Written explanations are exemplary. • Graphs are accurate and appropriate. • Goes beyond requirements of some or all problems.
3	**Satisfactory** A generally correct solution, but may contain minor flaws in reasoning or computation	• Shows an understanding of the concepts of *points on the coordinate plane, transformations, relations, functions, linear equations, arithmetic sequences,* and *patterns.* • Uses appropriate strategies to solve problems. • Computations are mostly correct. • Written explanations are effective. • Graphs are mostly accurate and appropriate. • Satisfies all requirements of problems.
2	**Nearly Satisfactory** A partially correct interpretation and/or solution to the problem	• Shows an understanding of most of the concepts of *points on the coordinate plane, transformations, relations, functions, linear equations, arithmetic sequences,* and *patterns.* • May not use appropriate strategies to solve problems. • Computations are mostly correct. • Written explanations are satisfactory. • Graphs are mostly accurate. • Satisfies the requirements of most of the problems.
1	**Nearly Unsatisfactory** A correct solution with no supporting evidence or explanation	• Final computation is correct. • No written explanations or work is shown to substantiate the final computation. • Graphs may be accurate but lack detail or explanation. • Satisfies minimal requirements of some of the problems.
0	**Unsatisfactory** An incorrect solution indicating no mathematical understanding of the concept or task, or no solution is given	• Shows little or no understanding of most of the concepts of *points on the coordinate plane, transformations, relations, functions, linear equations, arithmetic sequences,* and *patterns.* • Does not use appropriate strategies to solve problems. • Computations are incorrect. • Written explanations are unsatisfactory. • Graphs are inaccurate or inappropriate. • Does not satisfy requirements of problems. • No answer may be given.

Answers

Chapter 4 Assessment Answer Key

Page 273, Open-Ended Assessment
Sample Answers

In addition to the scoring rubric found on page A31, the following sample answers may be used as guidance in evaluating open-ended assessment items.

1a. Sample answer: $(-1, -1)$; quadrant III

1b. Sample answer: $(1, -1)$;

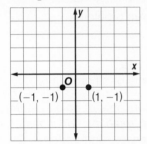

1c. The student should explain that knowing in which quadrant a point is located determines whether the point is to the right or left of the y-axis and above or below the x-axis, and thus, positive or negative.

2a. The four transformations are reflection, translation, dilation, and rotation. Depending on which two were chosen, the students may discuss whether the image and preimage are the same size, whether a line or point was used to assist the movement of the figure, whether the movement preserved the orientation or reversed the orientation of the figure.

2b. The student should discuss the characteristics of the two transformations that are the same. The student should discuss whether the transformations preserve size, direction, and orientation.

3a. Sample answer:
$\{(-1, -3), (0, -1), (1, 4), (2, 5)\}$;
$\{(-3, -1), (-1, 0), (4, 1), (5, 2)\}$

3b. Sample answer:

x	y
-1	-3
0	-3
0	-1
1	4
2	5

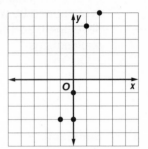

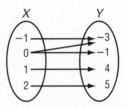

3c. The student should identify in their relation where they used the same domain element with two or more different range elements.

4. Sample answer: $x + y = 1$; To graph the equation find two solutions for the equation, plot the two points associated with the two solutions, and draw a straight line through the two points.

5. The value in the range that corresponds to the element 2 in the domain is represented by $f(2)$. The value $f(2)$ is found by substituting 2 for x in the equation.

6a. Sample answer: 2, 5, 8, 11, ... ;
The common difference is 3; $a_6 = 17$

6b. Sample answer: 5, 3, 8, 6, 11, 9, 14, ... ;
The pattern is to subtract 2 from the first term to find the second term, then add 5 to the second term to find the third term. Repeat the process of subtracting 2 then adding 5.

6c. The sequence 1, 1, 1, 1, ... is a set of numbers whose difference between successive terms is the constant number 0. Thus, this sequence is an arithmetic sequence by the definition.

Chapter 4 Assessment Answer Key

Vocabulary Test/Review
Page 274

1. axes

2. origin

3. quadrants

4. Transformations

5. translation

6. inverse

7. linear equation

8. function

9. vertical line test

10. the plane containing the *x*- and *y*-axes

11. a diagram that uses arrows to show how the elements of the domain of a relation are paired with elements of the range

Quiz (Lessons 4–1 and 4–2)
Page 275

1. ___(−3, 0); none___

2. ___(2, −4); IV___

3. ___rotation___

4. ___dilation___

5. $A'(-1, 2)$, $B'(-3, 3)$, $C'(-3, -1)$

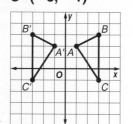

Quiz (Lessons 4–3 and 4–4)
Page 275

1.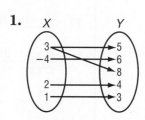

Domain: {−4, 1, 2, 3}
Range: {3, 4, 5, 6, 8}

2. {(−5, 2), (−3, −2), (1, 1), (4, −3)}; {(2, −5), (−2, −3), (1, 1), (−3, 4)}

3. {(−2, −11), (2, 5)}

4. {(−2, 0), (−1, 1.5), (0, 3), (2, 6), (3, 7.5)}

5. {(−3, −2), (−2, 0), (−1, 2), (0, 4), (1, 6)}

Quiz (Lessons 4–5 and 4–6)
Page 276

1. ___yes; $2x - y = 1$___

2.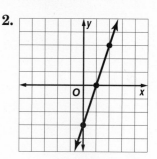

3. ___function___

4. ___30___

5. ___B___

Quiz (Lessons 4–7 and 4–8)
Page 276

1. ___no___

2. ___21, 25, 29___

3. ___25___

4. ___$5, 1, \dfrac{1}{5}$___

5. ___$f(x) = 2x - 2$___

Answers

Chapter 4 Assessment Answer Key

Mid-Chapter Test
Page 277

1. ___C___

2. ___B___

3. ___A___

4. ___D___

5. ___B___

6.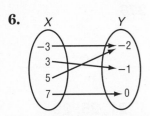

7. $D'(1, 1)$, $E'(4, 1)$, $F'(2, 4)$;
   See students' graphs.

8. $\{(-2, -7), (-1, -5),$
   $(0, -3), (2, 1), (3, 3)\}$

9. $\{(-3, 1), (0, 2),$
   $(3, 3), (6, 4)\}$:

Cumulative Review
Page 278

1. $\dfrac{4}{5}$

2. $8m + 9n$

3.

Stem	Leaf
0	5 8
1	0 2 2 2 2 2 5
2	0

$1|0 = 10$

4. ___6.16___

5. *x* divided by 4 minus *y*
   equals negative 2 times
   the quotient of *x* and *y*.

6. ___$12.75___

7. ___−2___

8. ___no___

9. $(-4, 3)$; II

10. $\{(-4, 3), (-4, -1),$
    $(-2, 2), (0, -1), (2, 3),$
    $(3, -3), (4, 1)\}$; domain:
    $\{-4, -2, 0, 2, 3, 4\}$;
    range: $\{-3, -1, 1, 2, 3\}$

11. ___not a function___

12. $A'(-1, 0)$, $B'(2, -4)$,
    $C'(3, -1)$

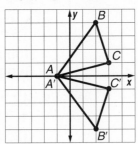

13. $\{(-3, -17), (-1, -9),$
    $(1, -1), (2, 3), (5, 15)\}$

14.

Chapter 4 Assessment Answer Key

Standardized Test Practice

Page 279

1. Ⓐ Ⓑ Ⓒ **Ⓓ**

2. Ⓔ **Ⓕ** Ⓖ Ⓗ

3. Ⓐ Ⓑ **Ⓒ** Ⓓ

4. **Ⓔ** Ⓕ Ⓖ Ⓗ

5. Ⓐ Ⓑ **Ⓒ** Ⓓ

6. Ⓔ Ⓕ Ⓖ **Ⓗ**

7. **Ⓐ** Ⓑ Ⓒ Ⓓ

8. Ⓔ **Ⓕ** Ⓖ Ⓗ

9. Ⓐ **Ⓑ** Ⓒ Ⓓ

10. Ⓔ Ⓕ **Ⓖ** Ⓗ

Page 280

11. **3 7**

12. **2 8**

13. **1 4**

14. **7 7**

15. Ⓐ Ⓑ Ⓒ **Ⓓ**

16. Ⓐ **Ⓑ** Ⓒ Ⓓ

17. **Ⓐ** Ⓑ Ⓒ Ⓓ

Glencoe Algebra 1

Answers